CW00940358

WINTER BIRDS

BLOOMSBURY WILDLIFE
Bloomsbury Publishing Plc
50 Bedford Square, London, WC1B 3DP, UK

BLOOMSBURY, BLOOMSBURY WILDLIFE
and the Diana logo are trademarks of
Bloomsbury Publishing Plc

First published by Bonnier Fakta, Stockholm, Sweden in 2015
First published in Great Britain 2017
Reprinted 2018

A catalogue record for this book is available from the British Library

ISBN: HB: 978-1-4729-6201-0; ePDF: 978-1-4729-4280-7; ePub: 978-1-4729-4279-1

2 4 6 8 10 9 7 5 3

Printed and bound in Latvia by Livonia Print

Lars Jonsson

WINTER BIRDS

B L O O M S B U R Y
LONDON • NEW DELHI • NEW YORK • SYDNEY

2mm

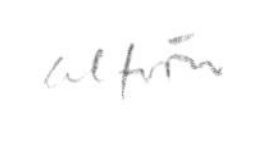
alfrön

2mm
alfrö

CONTENTS

FOREWORD

UNTIL NOW, MY WORK has concentrated on field guides. I worked my way systematically through all the bird species of Europe. Five volumes during the 1970s, arranged according to habitat or biogeographical regions, were combined into an identification guide in the 1980s. I remember, but chose to forget, how burdensome things can become at the end of this kind of work, when deadlines are approaching and just a few details are missing – details which, in the event, develop into a minor treatise.

In this book, my idea was to give an account of my impressions of bird species which could easily be seen from my studio window during the winter months. A simple book about a few species, with pictures which I have sketched out on the spot. It began with the Greenfinch; it was interest in and studies of different but quite normal Greenfinches that got me going. I wanted to show variations, expressions and colours of single individuals. After a couple of years of Greenfinch painting and studies I began to see a structure, how the work could be done. The problem was that there were 58 species missing which could all be given the same attention, which all had as many interesting differences and expressions which I considered worth showing and time was passing. A few days before the planned printing I find myself absorbed by the Fieldfares which have just arrived from the north, see new faces, find new characters which must be incorporated. That the book was completed is a wonder.

I wish first to thank my wife, Ragnhild, for her understanding and patience when I once more disappeared into a lengthy project. Thanks also to Martin, Annika and Pontus at the publishers for their patience and their gentle guidance towards the end result.

Lars Jonsson
Hamra, 11 november 2015

INTRODUCTION

LUCIA, 13 DECEMBER 2012. Over the last few days the snow cover has slowly increased and now a good 20 centimetres of snow lies over the landscape. It was 5 degrees below during the night and it feels as if the thermometer will stay well below zero. The sky is lead-grey and, according to the morning's weather forecast, there may be a little snow from the east during the day. I chose to put on overtrousers, as the route down towards the sea is unploughed after Lennart Ödman's farm. It will be a bit of a plod to make one's way down to the coastal meadows.

Now I am thinking of winter birds and the south Gotland countryside. The landscape is wintry and graphic. The light is not managing to penetrate properly and I am looking at the snow and trying to compare it with how a white surface would appear in March or April, the sort of thing that artists sometimes occupy themselves with – how white is white really?

White fields bordered by hedgerows of sloe, hawthorn and occasional crab apples. The snow is lying on the branches and only near the tips has the light breeze brushed out the twigs. Perched in our tangled honeysuckle bush is a small group of House Sparrows, pondering over what the day may bring. I placed a few hemp seeds on the wall there yesterday, but those not yet eaten are now covered by snow. House Sparrows in a winter bush are probably what I imagine to be the most wintry of all everyday bird scenes, a good start. Yesterday I logged on to the Swedish Ornithological Union's home page and downloaded the previous year's top 30 'Winter birds on our doorstep'. The union requests that Swedish people send in details of which birds they see at their birdfeeders during the last weekend in January. Nineteen-thousand birdtables have been counted and all the different species and their numbers combined into a national list showing the most common birds at seed-dispensers and fatballs across Sweden. This could be a good starting point in deciding which birds I should include in this book. But I allow myself the liberty of a personal choice and throw in some species which I particularly like and which I associate with winter.

Every year the lists are headed by the Great Tit, the most frequent of all birdtable visitors. This is due primarily to the fact that it is both numerous and generally widespread, but perhaps also that it does not hesitate to visit a solitary fatball or a small dispenser with sunflower seeds suspended from a window-ledge or balcony. The other places at the head of the list are taken by Tree Sparrow, Greenfinch, Yellowhammer, Blue Tit and Blackbird. Their relative positions have changed since the inventory began, in 2006, but the top 30 always include all those species which we associate with the winter birdtable: Nuthatch, Bullfinch, House Sparrow, Brambling and so on.

When I walk around the cowsheds and out on to the road, five Goldfinches are perched in some withered chicory plants along the wayside. This rather cheers me, partly because they turned up right now, partly because it reminds me that the species is in fact on the list of top species immediately below the twenty mark.

When one thinks of winter birds in general, it is to a large extent species which overwinter in the north and are adapted to snowy cold winters, such as Siberian Jay, Raven, Capercaillie, Golden Eagle, Willow Tit and Tawny Owl. Even some waterbirds are well able to overwinter so long as there is some open water and species such as Mallard, Goosander, Black-headed and Great Black-backed Gulls are often encountered on the coasts of Sweden during a winter stroll. Nevertheless, I have chosen to exclude all waterbirds, even though Mallard, Common Gull, Black-headed Gull and even Great Black-back are on the 'Winter birds on our doorstep' list. In many towns, organised feeding is carried out at park ponds, which are kept open in icy conditions by means of water pumps. These attract all manner of different ducks, gulls, corvids and buntings and a strict list of which birds can be thought to come to human-provided food does not of course exist. I have taken broadly the first sixty species in the most recent years' lists from 'Winter birds on our doorstep' and removed those birds which have webbed feet, that is the ducks and gulls. Then I have added Grey Partridge, a species which surprisingly enough is not included on any of the lists. Here in southern Gotland it is still relatively common and if we get snow and ice, especially if it freezes hard, this species readily comes into gardens bordering open fields. It is at home around active farmyards, and many times I have had Grey Partridges at my own feeding station.

The place where I feed the birds regularly is at my studio, a kilometre or so from our home. It is a converted barn at a farm which fell into disuse back at the end of the 1950s. It is situated beside a mature group of various broadleaf trees. Outside the studio window I have several large oaks, a large lime, several hazel stands and a series of various broadleaf trees such as Norway maple, ash, birch and a huge blackthorn shrubbery. It borders on an open wooded pasture where hawthorn, blackthorn and a few junipers form a background against the sea, which is visible several hundred metres down to the southeast. In the courtyard as I drive in to the studio there is a bushy area of cultivated plants, an old wild pear tree, lilacs, cherry trees, apple trees and plums which form a wall separating us from the neighbours, who are summer residents.

My prerequisites for feeding birds are probably somewhat different from those of most people. I live on a typical migration path between the regions in the northeast, Finland and Russia, and the wintering areas in the southwest, southern Sweden and west Europe. The five southernmost parishes on Gotland we call Storsudret, a land which forms a peninsula two-and-a-half miles long and a mile across at its widest point. In the middle of the peninsula is a continuous wooded area of pines and various broadleaf trees, but the country where I go is a markedly arable landscape with tilled land, fields, moor-like pastureland and scattered groves of trees. The tree grove by the studio is somewhat isolated from the central forest, therefore species such as the Coal Tit has never found its way here.

As I, not uncommonly, have Wood Pigeons and Stock Doves in the trees by the studio, both breeding here, the place becomes interesting also for raptors. The list of hunting birds which have been attracted to my feeding site, in other words those which have shown interest in my pigeons, buntings, woodmice and so on, is quite long. Golden Eagle, Goshawk, Sparrowhawk, Hen Harrier, Peregrine, Buzzard, Long-eared Owl and Great Grey Shrike. I have chosen to include three species of raptor, of which the Sparrowhawk is the most evident, but Goshawk and Buzzard are also present on the list of the sixty species which have been recorded during the winter bird counts. I often put out road-killed rabbits and hares or large pieces of bacon rind in order to attract models for my painting. Consequently, I have had Raven and Golden Eagle at food just some seventy metres from the studio. The Raven is otherwise the sort of bird which I believe has simply been attracted to food intended just for raptors. Perhaps they are merely visiting customary bird-feeding sites, but it may also be a matter of one or another Rook that has been misidentified. With the inclusion of the Raven in the book the presen-

tation of corvids is complete, which always feels good. Snow Bunting, Arctic Redpoll and Twite ('Winter Linnet') are all species which have a 'wintry' name and which for that reason seem naturals to be included in a book about winter birds, despite the fact that they are uncommon or rare visitors to birdtables. When it then became evident that they do, in any case, appear on the list of the top sixty in some years, the matter was settled. Snow Bunting I have seen at feeders on the doorstep in Lapland in spring and Twites apparently find their way to birdtables in other parts of Sweden.

I have chosen not to talk so much about how we feed birds or which kinds of seed and seed-dispensers are best; there is plenty on that in other publications. My interest and focus are the birds themselves, what they look like and how they behave, and their normal behaviour in winter. As an artist, I am occasionally fixated on their appearance and their colour pattern, something which happens naturally when I am constantly trying to interpret, with paintbrush and colour, what I see.

During the work on this book a number of previously acquired insights were intensified. One of these is that my own knowledge of many common species is imperfect. In order to paint a bird I must in some way find a connection with the species, link it to a specific occasion, or several, which we could call inspiration. When did I last draw a Grey-headed Woodpecker, or when did I last see a Nutcracker? It is not until I am going to paint a flying Jay that I really start to ponder what they actually look like, though I think that I already know that. When I then begin to look at Jays during their autumn acorn-gathering excursions I see the difference in the flight to the forest and that from the forest. On the journey back the flight is heavy and flappy, the course a little unsteady. On the way there it is straight and the wingbeats, if not clipped, still so much lighter and propelling. When I have to spell out the Hooded Crow's call, that constantly present croaking, I set about positioning myself in the yard on an early autumn morning with a notebook. Then a world upon which I have hardly reflected reveals itself. The countryside's crows seem to communicate with one another, short messages, they seem to 'twitter' about the state of things and their intentions for the day.

There are plenty of photographs on the internet and numerous books which describe many of the species which I deal with here. When I am to portray a particular species however, I have to find an observation of my own to get the process started. I need a clear visual picture which enables me to interpret my own photos or those of others. It is not enough to put together an average of several photographs; instead, I must have done a drawing of my own which becomes a model on which I can build details. The sketch is the key to the observation and, at the very end, it is my own observation that I wish to put across. Sometimes I think that I have had an artistic ornithological relationship with a particular species, but that it somehow petered out, or became unclear and then I have to make contact again, search it out. The Marsh Tit, which in my teens I knew so well from having grown up on the island of Södertörn, on the outskirts of Stockholm, seemed to have been erased or was not sufficiently vivid and so the painting came to a complete standstill, irrespective of how many photographs I searched out.

The fact that there were gaps in my knowledge about species which are absent in my everyday life here on south Gotland hardly surprised me. Part of my plan was to seek out some of these mainland species such as Crested Tit, Willow Tit and Marsh Tit. More surprising was the fact that, during the course of the work, I realised that even those species which I see daily can offer surprises and provide new lessons.

Recently I have reflected many times on how pleasing I still think it is simply to look at birds, after all these years. I hope to communicate this joy and the excitement I find in the observation itself of even the commonest species. How many thoughts and questions it raises about both their appearance and their biology. Yet this involves, to an equally high degree, questions about myself, my inner thoughts and what is important to me. I am driven by a powerful need to get close, to understand and interpret what I see and then to express this in the painting and the drawing.

The more one looks at a bird, the more questions arise. Björn von Rosen, in his book *Om naturtrohet och andra funderingar om konst* ('On faithfulness to nature and other thoughts on art'), stated that in order to see the invisible, one must learn to look properly at what is visible. If one looks at the everyday things for long enough, then the ordinary and the plain things that we have all around us stand out as unique. It is this sense and feeling that I wish to put across in this book.

The prospect of winter

For most people autumn is a relative concept, arriving when we think that the summer is set to end: quite simply, that day when the summer feeling seems to have gone. Often we can feel the way things are going as early as August, when the evenings begin to draw in and dew collects on the grass. I often think of autumn when the first clear September air makes itself felt, when the heat transfer at night lowers the temperature by several degrees and everything looks crisp outside. A first '*click*' from a Robin, a '*hueet tick-tick*' from a Redstart stopping off in the garden or a new Spotted Flycatcher perched in the wild pear tree, all small feathered signs telling that autumn is here. It may still be August, but one has an inner feeling that the first frost has arrived in the north. Now not only have the warblers begun to migrate southwards but the first thrushes, too, have already started their journey.

September, the first 'official' month of autumn according to the almanac, can be regarded in pure meteorological terms as a summer month in south Sweden, in the same way as the winter often arrives as early as October in Lapland. According to the Swedish Meteorological and Hydrological Institute (SMHI), autumn should fall on the first of five consecutive days which show a mean temperature below 10°c. For birds which live mainly on insects this is a pretty good benchmark, as insect numbers rapidly decrease when autumn arrives. In Kiruna, in extreme north Sweden, this happens around mid-August and most warblers and Pied Flycatchers have then left the northern forests. Certainly, there will still be mild days with flying insects in the north, but evolution has forcibly carved out a behaviour which secures the survival of the passerines which migrate to the tropics. For some species, such as the Garden Warbler or the Blackcap, there is time to linger a while longer, as they can change over to eating berries on days when the autumn's arrival makes itself felt. However, for seed-eating birds, such as finches and buntings, autumn is harvest time. When berries and seed-heads have ripened on trees and smaller plants towards late summer, this signifies that the dining tables are full and the supplies generally last throughout the winter. As early as May, Linnets can be seen dissecting the closed 'pixie-caps' of the dandelions in order to pluck out the barely ripe seeds, and the plants' seed-setting and ripening continue thus right through the summer.

Tit flocks

Everybody who strolls through the woods in late summer and into autumn is well aware of the silence. The feeling of emptiness, or the absence of life, often becomes obvious with the early summer's sound – picture fresh in the memory. Towards high summer tits, Treecreepers, Nuthatches and Goldcrests are already gathering in small groups, known as 'roving tit flocks', which move around the local area. Should one catch sight of such a flock, the trees all around can suddenly come to life with the birds' calls and the rustling of branches. These tit flocks have a clear structure and consist partly of birds which may move in groups through large sections of the landscape and partly of birds which are very sedentary but which latch on to a flock when it passes through their territory. In coniferous and mixed forest such flocks can consist of Willow Tit, Crested Tit, Goldcrest, Treecreeper and Great Tit. In many clumps of trees and deciduous areas around villages and suburbs it is often the Great Tit and Blue Tit that make up the core of the group, with one or two Nuthatches as animated supporters.

Willow Warblers and flycatchers will often be part of these apparently roving flocks at the outset. For those species which remain in one place over the winter, the behaviour should be termed 'patrolling', since they are taking stock of the area, foraging and guarding their patch or territory. Birds with different food requirements and different plans for the winter naturally collect within hearing distance of one another after the breeding season ends. Such a group can contain several Great Tits and Blue Tits which later move in towards the village, some woodland tits which intend to stay in one place throughout their life, a Treecreeper and a pair of local Nuthatches, and perhaps a Great Spotted Woodpecker. Birds can benefit from one another's vision and hearing when faced with approaching danger. It is not uncommon to see Jays around tit flocks, or perhaps it is the tits that are drawn to the Jays as sentinels and protectors. The great advantage of living in a group is surveillance. If any individual sees the silhouette of a Sparrowhawk or discovers a Pygmy Owl, all are immediately made aware of the danger.

Winter stores

The prerequisite for overwintering is, of course, access to food. For the hardiest species such as grouse and some finches, the needles and buds of trees can constitute a sufficient food base for them to remain in the forest. Other species lay up stores of the autumn's crop and are then able to make use of these during the lean days of winter. Such exploiters of nature include Nuthatch, Jay and many tits, which gather in the barns at the approach of winter. In their case the 'barn' is the forest with its ground structure and its trees full of nooks and crannies. In bark crevices and branch crotches, among needles and in cones and lichens, tits can stow away seeds in summer and autumn and also create supplies of insects, which they utilise during the winter. A single large spruce certainly contains millions of small morsels of edible animal food in the form of insects and spiders which had sought a hibernation site – small invertebrates which either had found their way there of their own accord or had been stowed away there by a tit. Some cover their own hiding-places with a bit of lichen.

If you take home a spruce branch or a rotten piece of branch in winter and place a table-lamp above it, you may be surprised by the number of different creepy-crawlies that start to come to life, awakened from their hibernation. While the Nutcrackers remember where they have hidden all of their hazelnuts, perhaps the alpha pair of Willow Tits does not recollect fully but knows in which specific part of the trees, at what height and in what section of the branches it has hidden its food. Then the tits defend this segment and forage within it throughout the winter, and probably then come across their own caches.

There are, of course, natural supplies of food all winter for certain species. Where I live there is an abundance of ash trees, and if seed-setting is good it is easy to imagine that several species such as Bullfinch, Great Tit and Blue Tit have a full larder. Seed-heads remain through the winter and even if the snow cover is deep, they can profit from their seeds. The maple's seeds, on the other hand, always fall to the ground and are easily accessible only so long as there is no snow, or no more than a thin covering of snow, on the ground. An important food source for woodland bird species is seed from pine and spruce. Coal Tit, crossbills, Great Spotted Woodpecker and Siskin are species which are dependent on these seeds, but Chaffinches, too, eat fallen spruce seeds in the spring in northern regions. Most finches prefer energy-rich seeds from plants and trees, but when these run short, which often happens in late winter, they may change to eating buds from bushes and trees.

Residents and migrants

Many species treated in this book are genuine residents which spend their entire life in the area in which they settled as adults. Other species which we often regard as pure residents undertake extensive movements during autumn from the northernmost parts of their breeding range, examples being the Bullfinch, Blackbird and Sparrowhawk. Several species which change to a berry diet, such as Waxwing, thrushes, Robin and Blackcap, may linger a bit longer if the berry supply is good. Species which in part overwinter, but which move over wide areas during winter and whose migratory movements are by and large governed by food supply and the weather, were earlier called migrants. Birds such as the Siskin and Brambling migrate out of their breeding areas in the north, but may stay largely in southern Scandinavia if there is sufficient food. Their winter behaviour is nomadic; in some winters they are found in large numbers in an area, only to be entirely absent there in the next winter. Our best-known winter bird, the Great Tit, could really be described as partially migratory. It gives up its own territory in summer and roams around with others of its species in the area. If it comes upon a suitable food source, a beech grove, a clump of oaks or a pine plantation with good seed set, it stays and settles down in the area. But this can just as well be a garden where somebody feeds the birds regularly.

Some species, such as the Wren and Goldcrest, are dependent in winter on hibernating spiders and insect pupae and will often take a chance: in other words, they attempt to stay put in the hope of a mild winter. This is a strategy which can pay off if we get a series of mild winters, but one which can have severely punishing consequences if the winter cold becomes protracted. The Wren seeks its prey in cracks and hiding-places among brushwood, pine needles, branches and withered plant brush: it is laborious work if the snow buries or covers these small larders for a lengthy period. The Goldcrests search in a similar way for insects and spiders among the branches of spruces and pines.

Moult and age determination

Most birds will undergo a change of plumage, a moult of the feathers, after the breeding season. For each species there is a clear moult pattern, a general time schedule, but the timing can vary depending on external circumstances and it is important in any case to have fresh feathers before the coming winter months. For adult birds the norm is that all the feathers are renewed, which is known as complete moult.

Among the passerines, many young of the year, or juveniles, change only the body and head feathers together with the lesser wing-coverts, and retain the tail feathers and flight-feathers, this being known as a partial moult. With a few species, such as the Starling and House Sparrow, the juveniles have a complete moult and thereafter become almost impossible to recognise as immature birds. Juveniles which have a partial moult may also change all or some of the greater coverts. With some species, such as the Greenfinch, which perhaps has three broods, the young of the final brood will, like the parents, be late in starting the moult and perhaps not complete it until into October. Others, hatched early in the season, have more time for moulting and perhaps also renew one or a pair of the innermost secondaries (the tertials) and the central tail feathers.

In the case of birds of prey, the young never renew any of their juvenile feathers immediately after fledging but wait until the following spring and therefore remain juvenile in plumage during their first winter. Typical of many finches is that the summer (or breeding) plumage is gained by means of feather abrasion. This involves the new feathers which grow

Greenfinch, adult male

wing of adult male

wing of young female Greenfinch with worn tertials

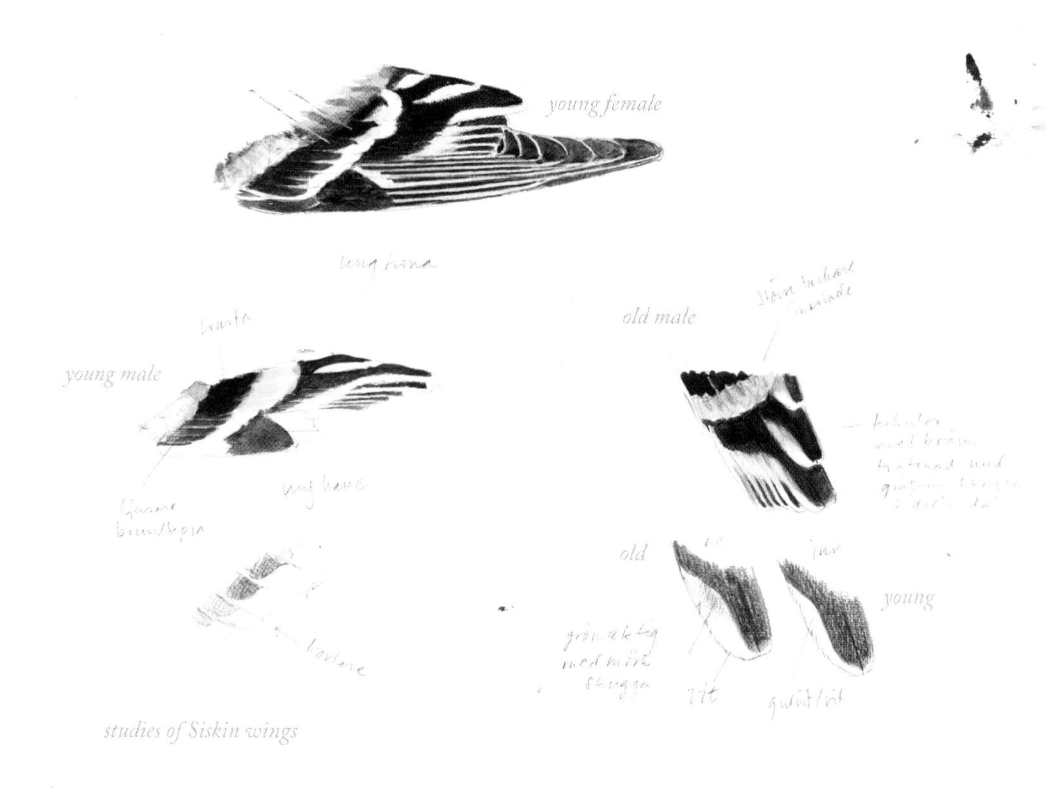

studies of Siskin wings

in the autumn, having an outer fringe which conceals the more brightly coloured parts. Towards the spring these fringes, often brown and light buff in colour, have become so weak that they are broken or worn off, thus revealing the underlying black or more more strongly coloured tones. Bramblings and Chaffinches assume a plumage which makes them blend in among dead leaves and withering plants, while the Yellowhammers' yellow colours are partly concealed by colours borrowed from wilting grass. All tits and Bullfinches make no distinction between autumn and spring but are much the same in coloration throughout the year.

Often it is possible to recognise immature birds by the fact that there is a difference in wear and colour pattern between the juvenile feathers and the new 'adult' feathers grown in through a partial moult. It is usually necessary to see the birds at very close range and, if you take photographs, it is easiest to see this on an enlarged picture. It can be interesting to know whether the Blackbird or the Siskin which you see, is a young bird or an adult.

Maps

The purpose of the maps in this book is to give a rough picture of where it is likely or, rather, possible that the species can be seen at a birdtable in winter. It is considerably more difficult to create a true picture of a species' winter distribution than it is for its breeding range. For people who put out food between October and April the species list will, moreover, be increased by several passing migrants, such as the Brambling, Dunnock and Robin, even right up in north Sweden.

I have made use of data from the 'Species portal' which is run by the Swedish University of Agricultural Sciences in Uppsala. On this portal it is possible to search for reports of a species according to certain search criteria. I looked for observations from December to February during the years 2010 to 2015. The reports refer to general observations, not specifically at feeding stations. It appears then, that many normally migratory passerines were seen as single individuals over wide areas and can theoretically therefore turn up at birdtables. The Dunnock is one such species which, by reason of that, has a large winter distribution, but is in fact very rare in winter outside Scania and Halland, in extreme south Sweden. Stock Dove and Wood Pigeon are species which often return as early as the end of February in central Sweden but are uncommon as genuine winterers. Other species may linger into December after a mild autumn but perhaps are not able to survive through the whole winter.

There are many explanations for why the maps do not always reflect normal presence during the winter months and they should be seen more as a guide. They overstate the occurrence of several normally migratory species, but are more accurate for the most commonly occurring birdtable species. In the species texts I have attempted to give a truer picture of their actual status in winter. Sources for the other nordic countries are *Norsk Vinterfugleatlas* (Norwegian winter-bird atlas) and *Fuglenes Danmark* (Denmark Birds). There is no comprehensive account of winter distributions for Finland, so I have made use of *The Finnish Bird Ringing Atlas Vol. II*, as well as other sources. The maps are actually, I confess, a graphic element in the book since I do have a childlike fondness for maps, especially hand-drawn ones. The population figures are taken from the book *Fåglarna i Sverige* (Birds in Sweden), published by Sveriges Ornitologiska Förening (Swedish Ornithological Union).

Lönnnäsor
Agorta 24.10.15

THE BIRD SPECIES

GREY PARTRIDGE

Perdix perdix

THE GREY PARTRIDGE does not feature among the 60 bird species topping the 'Winter birds on our doorstep' list, i.e. the winter birds that are most common at our birdtables. It is nevertheless a regular visitor quite close to the house where I live, in a distinctly agricultural landscape with fields and wooded pasture in south Gotland. Around the active farmyards there are lots of edge zones and areas of ground compacted by frequent farm-machinery movements, which harbour plenty of knotgrass and annual meadow-grass, which Grey Partridges love. As early as autumn a small family party will appear in our courtyard. Then they come sneaking in through the hole in the gate and check if the garden plot has anything edible and exposed surfaces to bathe in. Undisturbed, they are continuously on the go as, with rapid movements, they nip off the tops of grass and weeds. When snow covers the ground their presence is more obvious. They are then often found on open fields, where they eat green leaves of autumn-sown rape or rye. If the winter weather gets really cold, windy and with lots of snow and they are unable to dig down to the ground level, one can count on their being regular visitors at any feeding site. It is usually family groups consisting of a pair and its young, which keep together during the winter and the group will not split up until they take up territories some time at the end of March.

The Grey Partridge has the body size of a small farmyard hen or, perhaps better, a crow. It is nicely rounded in shape and its plumage is a marvel of markings and vermiculations, an echo of a meagre tilled patch in fallow land. The male has a brighter and more extensively rose-hip-soup-coloured face and a bigger horse-chestnut-coloured belly patch than the female. The dark horizontal markings over the entire back and rump have a clearer brownish-red tone, the corresponding area on the female being brownish. The female's face is usually easy to recognise in winter by the more old-fashioned expression, with a greyish eyebrow

and a grey border to the orange-red mask. Altogether, the females look slightly more grey and buff compared with the males.

This partridge thrives only in fully open terrain with herb-rich edge zones which imitate the steppe landscape where the species originally evolved. In Sweden it is strongly tied to flat lowlands in the southern parts of the country. Since the Grey Partridge is normally a pronounced sedentary species not inclined to fly longish distances, its occurrence on Gotland is a result of introduction, its present population stemming probably from the 1820s. The species is known however, from archaeological excavations from the fifth century on Öland and Gotland, having probably been brought there by traders. Its numbers have fluctuated strongly over time, as harsh winters can almost wipe out an isolated population. In Russia, Grey Partridges may undertake lengthy movements if ice and ice-crusted snow prevent them from reaching plants in the ground-layer. The species has, however, found its way by natural means to the Baltic Sea region in the wake of man's cultivation of the landscape. It is likely

that the population reached its peak around the 1950s, when the climate became warmer and many predators, such as Goshawk and fox, were greatly reduced by persecution. In Denmark, 300,000 to 400,000 Grey Partridges were shot annually during the 1950s: however, introductions for the purpose of hunting were widespread. The population has not been favoured by modern agriculture, as widespread use of weed-killers and insecticides reduces the birds' food supply. For the first few days the young are dependent on insects. The decline increased after the 1960s, and the species is now usually rare in occurrence in central Sweden.

In my neighbourhood I usually see birds still in pairs throughout May and juvenile broods not until high summer, from midsummer onwards, and quite young birds not uncommonly into August. It is probably usual for the first broods to come to nothing, or else the species has gradually become adapted to egg-laying at a later date when grazing pastures have grown again after the first hay-making, in May.

COMMON PHEASANT

Phasianus colchicus

THE COMMON PHEASANT was introduced into Europe from populations originating in various regions of Asia, from the Caucasus to China. The introduction began in Sweden in the middle of the 1700s, but not until the end of the 1800s did the stock get a proper foothold in south Sweden. Within the species' natural range there is a large number of races and colour variants. The most commonly occurring birds display a mixture of characters of different races. The race which has given the species its scientific name, the nominate race *colchicus*, which breeds closest to us in Transcaucasia, lacks a neck-collar and has a more coherent range of colours with orange and russet tones. The one from China, *torquatus*, has a beautiful blue-grey colour on the rump and lesser wing-coverts. Swedish birds usually exhibit a white neck-ring but rarely have a distinct blue-grey colour tone. Sometimes seen are dark variants of the race *tenebrosus* in which dark blue and green replace the orange and reddish-purple tones, a colour variant which also originates from China.

The females are distinctly smaller than the males and look generally brownish-buff, but they show a nice ornamentation which gives me as a painter more inspiration than the showy males do. The dark blue-green morph has an equivalent in the females, which have a more dark red-brown or chestnut-brown ground colour. The males' exposed red skin on the head varies through the year and also among individuals, depending on their condition and status.

Pheasants have through the ages been introduced as gamebirds and this still happens on many large estates. In Scotland they are so common locally that they are thought of as domestic fowl and it is possible that populations in Sweden would gradually disappear after recurrent cold winters if new releases were not continually being made. The pheasant is found in farmland, on open fields and arable land adjoining woodland edges and bushy areas and often close to wetlands with reeds. The

feather study of tenebrosus male

birds often visit birdtables and are actively fed on estates where pheasant-shooting is pursued as an economic enterprise. I have myself periodically had visits from pheasants at my feeding station, which is situated beside a small wood with various broadleaf trees.

Pheasants roost like hens on a perch, i.e. on a branch up in a tree, but preferably in a dense blackthorn shrubbery or a spruce plantation where they are sheltered from Goshawks, their primary enemy. If a fox comes along, they immediately fly up on to a branch.

Serious courtship

In years when I have had pheasants all around the studio site, I have been amused by the cocks' courtship of the females. The male displays his entire upperside by angling his body towards the female and spreading it so that it forms a carpet of every colour and pattern. The tail is spread like a fan. The male positions himself constantly in the way of the female as if he wishes to force her to behold his finery, like an unusually insistent carpet salesman. At the beginning of spring the female appears uninterested by the male's courting and continues to eat, but I assume that the further the spring advances, the more she will think that he is, after all, quite handsome. The territorial call is performed best from a slight elevation in the terrain. The male stands up and gives a distinctively hoarse '*che-veck*' cry rapidly followed by a wing-rustling. The fact that pheasants and other gallinaceous birds have developed extreme feather patterns and shapes is not just a manifestation of the females' interest in general ornamentation. The more extreme tail or colour markings a male has, the greater capacity for survival he is considered to have and this is often an indication that the male has what is needed in order to give the offspring the proper hereditary factors.

The females in turn are immensely cryptic in their pattern and when they are sitting among dead grass, plants and branches one realises that their plumage has a definite purpose. The surroundings in which I see my pheasants most likely bear similarities to the natural broadleaf forests from which the species originates. When the female walks through a thicket she is as if swallowed up by her background, as if she were just a part of a carpet brought from some central Asian mountain slope.

If we examine the female's individual feathers at close range, they are put together in an extremely advanced and tasteful way, but whether this is just an echo of the male's markings or gives some additional dimension in the social life is difficult to answer. As camouflage, a less ambitious pattern would presumably do just as well.

As an illustrator of the movements and shapes of birds, I am fascinated by the construction of facial forms of the pheasants and partridges. Where the male looks mostly over-decorated, the female has produced a number of sculptural elements which form subocular bags, cheek pouches, eyebrows and various bands of feather rows as if they had been constructed from strips of rolled clay. When the head is bent downwards towards the ground, these shapes manifest themselves in different ways dictated by perspective. This lends much character to the face but is frustrating to depict and it is easy to get it wrong.

young male

SPARROW HAWK

Accipiter nisus

SUDDENLY THE TREE SPARROWS stop their chatter and sweep like brown autumn leaves into the rose bush, the Great Tits 'freeze' on their branches and the Greenfinches explode in all directions. A Blackbird, emitting a furious staccato in remonstration, flees into a blackthorn shrubbery ten metres away. A Sparrowhawk shoots on closed wings like an arrow into the idyllic scene, twists its body and opens its wings and tail, makes a couple of lightning-fast turns and then a neat slower sweep like a paper aeroplane before landing with a spread tail on the rose bushes. A yellow eye gazes down into the shrubbery where the Tree Sparrows had hurriedly moved down a level. One more failed attempt from the Sparrowhawk. It attacks the bush from a couple of different directions, runs around on the ground and pushes its way in, but only to see the Tree Sparrows quickly move to the other side. He gives up and moves a few metres upwards in the lime tree, shakes his wings and settles, his long slender legs and long yellow finger-like talons clearly visible. He perches there for a minute so as to see if some unwary bird comes back. But his hunting attempt failed and now he waits for the visitors to the birdtable to lower their state of high alert. But in all probability it is all over. Older hawks perch more rarely in or near the hunting area itself after a failed attempt; they immediately dash off to the next one.

The male Sparrowhawk is much smaller than the female, a difference clearly visible in the field. A male is only 50 per cent of the female's weight, and is 20 per cent smaller in length. This means that the two can exploit different prey within the territory. It is more common to see young birds hunting at food-provisioning sites. These birds are generally browner above and have, to a varying degree, rusty-yellow or rusty-brown fringes on the upperpart feathers and a broader white supercilium. On the upper breast they have more longitudinally arranged spots, often drop-shaped or heart-shaped, giving a more spotted impression

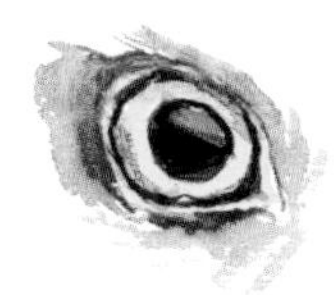

than on the older birds. The immatures vary quite a lot in their colour range and paleness and males especially can be markedly rusty-toned. The upperpart feathers, primarily the scapulars, wing-coverts and tertials, usually have large white spots near the base which seem to be more pronounced on immatures. When resting they ruffle up the feathers and often look strongly variegated on the back. When they then become alert and sleek their plumage, these spots are concealed. Some immatures have poorly developed warm-coloured fringes and can be hard to distinguish from adult females, especially in spring when these fringes can be completely worn away. Drop-shaped spots on the breast may also have faded or been worn off so that the underlying basal parts, which have more crosswise markings, are exposed. They then become very like the older females. Adult females normally have a more neutral grey tone on the upperside, a narrower supercilium and more distinct and neat barring below. Females, too, can have clear elements of fox-red markings, especially on the cheeks and flanks. When the immatures moult in the spring and summer of their second calendar-year, they become like the adults however, it is common for occasional juvenile feathers in the wing and tail to be retained over the second winter. These browner and more worn feathers can then reveal the bird's age.

The handsome male

The sight of an older male is often suprising, as it seems almost exotic with its beautiful blue-grey upperside and fox-red underside. The colour of the upperparts is, to a varying degree, dark grey or mid-grey, but appears as blue-grey since blue and orange are complementary colours. The males have an almost black border to the eye, like a black eye, which continues back over the ear-coverts, while the lore, the area between the bill and the eye, is whitish. Every time I happen across an adult male with a really rust-red underside I am equally surprised at its display of colour. Often it is during the spring passage from the end of March and just into April that they turn up very briefly. The amount of red on the underparts and chin varies individually, as does the presence of a thin supercilium and a pale patch on the nape. Some males completely lack a supercilium and nape patch and this seems not to have anything to do with age.

Dropfläck
bröst ung Sparvhök
bröstfjäder
gammal hona
male
female

The hunter of small birds

The Sparrowhawk is the passerines' worst enemy in winter. It is a true small-bird specialist with very long tarsi and a long middle toe which can reach in and grasp prey inside the vegetation. Its tactics are almost always those of surprise; the hawks begin the hunt from a distance, whereby they speed up and glide in towards the prey under cover of a building or vegetation. If the first attempt fails, it is rare for them to succeed by means of repeated attacks around feeding stations. A healthy bird usually has the advantage. Birds often come to grief against window panes near birdtables when they flee and see a sky reflected in the glass or an escape route between two opposite windows. During all the years in which I have watched Sparrowhawks at my birdtable, I have seen how individuals differ in their manner of hunting. In one period, I had a birdtable of the half-timbered-house type with doorways where the seeds drop out. The openings were big enough for a Tree Sparrow to enter. A young Sparrowhawk made rapid aerial approaches towards the house and perched on its roof. He then hung by his claws from the rim and moved with rapid sideways shifts around the table in order to see if any sparrow was still inside. Presumably this was a display of flexibility, an ability to adapt its hunting techniques to the current situation. It all looked quite comical, however, and I felt a certain sympathy for that particular bird.

Our most common bird of prey

The Sparrowhawk is a common breeder in woodlands and parks throughout Sweden and is the most numerous of the country's birds of prey, followed closely by the Common Buzzard. The Swedish population is estimated at about 45,000 pairs. It is absent in open upland terrain, where the Merlin takes over as the the small-bird specialist. It does well in towns and villages if there are suitable parks or wooded stretches where it can nest and has a preference for denser spruce stands as breeding habitat. It is mainly a migrant in the northern parts of its range, while the majority remain through the winter in southernmost Scandinavia. Immatures linger to a greater extent in southern and central Sweden and then often overwinter close to villages, where the supply of passerines is greater than in adjacent woodland tracts. Is is most usual, therefore, that a Sparrowhawk visiting a feeding station is a young bird.

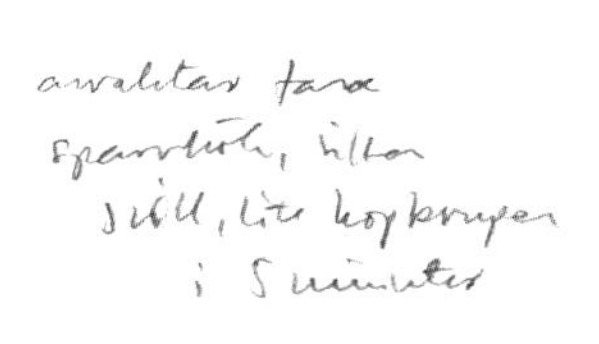

GOSHAWK

Accipiter gentilis

THE GOSHAWK has in recent times moved into the city and to some extent driven the Sparrowhawk out of urban environments. The species was systematically persecuted throughout the 1900s because it took not only domestic hens but also other game species which were sought after by humans. In his book *Skandinavisk fauna* (1858), the renowned natural historian Sven Nilsson, based in Scania, wrote that in that part of south Sweden it was one of the most common and most 'noxious' raptors. Over all the years, I have always found the Goshawk to be a markedly shy bird, and older birds especially will rarely appear as artist's models at a reasonable distance. Usually just brief encounters are the rule, a steel-grey back gliding among trees, or over the forest road.

With Goshawks of the new generation, which are at home in parks and among buildings, things are different. On several occasions in recent years, I have been driving my car in Stockholm when a hunting Goshawk happens to pass over a roundabout or between the planted lime trees in the roadway and I am always equally surprised. In the centre of Stockholm, in winter, the Goshawk usually hunts Black-headed Gulls at the Strömmen or pigeons around the houses bordering Kungsträdgården (the King's Court). It is almost always crows that announce its presence, in town and country and they yell with great irritation in the voice when they discover a Goshawk. The pitch is totally different from that when a Sparrowhawk is about. Despite its adaptation to the 'stone city' (Sundsvall), for breeding the Goshawk requires areas with slightly older woodland, of which today almost more is found in the suburbs of cities than out in the commercial forest which dominates the country's forested regions.

An adult male Goshawk is a revelation with its orange-red or sometimes fully red eye. The face of the older male is often rich in contrasts, with a dark slate-grey or blackish crown and ear-coverts. The barring on

female

male

the underside seems to become finer in pattern with age and less black in tone, so that the bird can look very pale, almost whitish, below.

The female is considerably larger than the male and often weighs 1.5 kilos. Females have a bright yellow eye, less contrast in the face, the yellow on the cere is often not very conspicuous and they look more uniformly grey-faced. The upperparts are often less pure grey but the individual differences are quite big and the sexes can look very alike. The Goshawk's dark slate-grey or grey feathers become browner with wear and so one can sometimes see individuals which are partially browner on the back. The male's lower back and rump however, have a nice neutral grey tone, noticeable when it glides past at high speed low down. A male in his first adult plumage (second winter) usually has the same eye colour as the female and coarser barring below. Often one or more juvenile remiges are retained, these differ in their browner colour. The breast barring on these 'second-years' is often in the form of shallow V-markings.

It is easy to confuse the Goshawk and the Sparrowhawk in flight, especially the male Goshawk and female Sparrowhawk, at a quick glance. The similarity in markings and outward shape of the wings can cause confusion. But the weight of a Goshawk makes it look much more stable in flight compared with a Sparrowhawk, the body gliding forwards on a straighter path, whereas the Sparrowhawk's relatively light weight makes its flight appear more flapping, more unstable. The Goshawk has, in addition, a more rounded tail with a broader pale terminal band.

The juvenile is brown above, often strongly patterned in pale buff or rusty buff. Wide variation exists and some eastern birds can be very pale

immature
young male

and strongly variegated above. The Goshawk is always however, streaked over the entire belly and breast and only occasionally are horizontally arranged spots to be seen on the flank feathers. In comparison with a young Sparrowhawk the face is completely different, the Goshawk's eye seeming to be positioned farther back and situated in a lightly streaked, relatively pale face, lacking the Sparrowhawk's darker setting. The young Goshawk, moreover, has a pattern of streaks on the middle of the throat (the chin) which, when seen from in front, form a characteristic dark band. The greater secondary coverts, i.e. right across the middle of the folded wing, are pale at the base almost throughout, so that a pale, variegated band is formed which is the palest part of the wing and back.

The forest's hunters

The Goshawk and the Sparrowhawk are in many ways ultimate birds of prey in woodland, where the relatively short and broad wings, in combination with a long tail, facilitate great manoeuvring capacity at high speed in closed habitats. The Goshawk can make its way at good speed though very narrow spaces in the branches in pursuit of a Jay or squirrel. It is the larger of the two and has evolved to be able to profit from heavier prey such as Black Grouse, Capercaillie, Wood Pigeon and Jay. The Sparrowhawk hunts mainly passerines. On the ground, the Goshawk also uses its powerful legs to move very fast and adeptly over short distances in order to pursue a quarry underneath bushes. I have myself observed this when on a couple of occasions I have been called upon to extract a Goshawk from a hen coop: it can shoot away like a bullet.

Even though the Goshawk is basically a forest bird, it often hunts in open terrain and over wetlands. It freely kills ducks directly in the water and I once saw a male kill a Long-tailed Duck, a prey species which required the hawk to remain lying on the water for several minutes with its wings spread before the duck could be gathered up. Because the sexes of both hawk species differ in size, the pair is able to profit from a broader supply of prey species. Consequently there is, to a certain extent, an overlap in food selection between the female Sparrowhawk and the male Goshawk.

adult male

BUZZARD

Buteo buteo

THE BUZZARD is one of our most common and most often seen birds of prey. There are about 30,000 pairs in Sweden, the majority in south and central Sweden. It requires mature forest or at least groves of trees for breeding, but it forages mostly on open fields and arable land or in clearings. Unlike the two hawk species, it has not found its way into cities and avoids larger communities. During the breeding season it usually becomes more anonymous and more tied to woodland. Its diet consists of smaller mammals, mostly rodents and shrews, but it takes frogs, snakes, worms and insects, too. The Buzzard often lives during the non-breeding season in open cultivated country, where it likes to perch on fences and telephone poles on the lookout for voles. It readily finds a productive edge zone quite close to the road, a bank or a ditch which often harbours small rodents. In north and large parts of central Sweden the Buzzard is a migrant which spends the winter in west Europe, south to France. However, many are residents in the southern provinces and in winter their numbers are added to by juveniles from the north.

Owl-like silhouette

A generally dark brown bird of prey with a broad and rounded head shape perched along the roadside, a little owl-like in silhouette, is almost always a Buzzard. In flight the wings are broad and rounded, with a pale band across the base of the primaries and secondaries, these are often glistening whitish colour when the bird is flying over snow.

The adults are easily recognised by their dark coffee-brown eyes which look black at a distance, contrasting a little with a greyish eyering and lore. The juveniles initially have a markedly pale iris, which darkens during the winter, but they always retain a paleness during the first year so that the black pupil is clearly visible.

The Buzzard varies greatly in markings and can be predominantly pale, whitish or light buffish-yellow, with limited dark markings. The most common form however, is mostly dark brown with a paler girdle of transverse bands under the breast and dark-spotted white vent. The male is generally darker and more evenly dark brown than the female. To a varying extent he has paler streaks on the throat and centrally on the breast and belly. Older birds typically do not renew all of the wing coverts or scapular feathers at the same time and a contrast is therefore visible, with older, slightly faded feathers or feather tips, irregularly interspersed in the dark brown ones. The younger birds, during their first winter, are generally more streaked below and often have paler markings on the large median secondary coverts and the scapulars. The feather markings form more regular patterns over the back.

Food for Buzzards

If you wish to have one or more Buzzards visiting your residence, you should 'cater' especially for the species. I have often had a Buzzard visit even larger bits of suet or bacon rind which had been fixed up on a branch or trunk, especially when it is cold with plenty of snow. If you have Buzzards nearby in winter, which is of course a prerequisite, you should provide carrion on an exposed surface a little away from the house. Meat, offal, bacon rind, dead game animals, are all fine. I am probably not the only one who has bought half a pig, the less vital parts of which have lain far too long in the freezer. Road-killed hares and rabbits also end up in my freezer, just so that I shall be able to entice suitable subjects for paintings. Where I live it is always Magpies and crows that are first to arrive on site, but it is seldom long before a Buzzard finds its way there too.

I regularly see the Buzzard showing interest in the birdtable even if there are only seed and fatballs there. Often it arrives unobtrusively, gliding in to the trees close to the studio. After having checked that the coast is clear, it flies in close to where the food is. Probably its interest is at first directed at the shrews which regularly feed there, or sometimes a solitary brown rat. One particular individual however, seemed

immature

to wait for the Sparrowhawk to come and attack the small birds. On several occasions when I heard the birds take flight and I went to the window, a Buzzard flew up from the ground. Such was the case every time a passerine flew into my window pane. Whether the raptor itself deliberately scared a bird to fly into the pane or whether this was a subsidiary effect of a hunting attempt I was never able to judge. On various occasions however, the Buzzard suddenly appeared precisely when the Sparrowhawk by chance happened to fly in to the picture. I was never able to verify that it was a deliberate hunting technique to exploit the Sparrowhawk's attacks. I felt that we had a certain relationship, the Buzzard and I. When I came to the window, it checked me for a second and then flew away, but it was very soon back again.

DOMESTIC PIGEON

Columba livia (domest.)

THE DOMESTIC PIGEON hardly arouses any great curiosity among birdwatchers in general and I am not an exception. When I try to imagine what I can say about this species, my thoughts are inexorably drawn to its wild variant, the Rock Dove *Columba livia*. The Rock Dove is the origin of all of today's domestic and carrier pigeons. It is acknowledged as a 'real' species, a bird which one can, as a field ornithologist, imagine looking for and studying. In my sketchbooks the domestic pigeon is conspicuous by its absence and I could recollect only a single study which I had done in the field. This was a 'carrier pigeon' of mixed brown colours which settled a metre in front of me at Stenshuvud, in southeast Scania, a good thirty years ago. It sat for a long time and looked mysteriously at me as if it wanted to communicate something important. As for me, I was busy listening for Tawny Pipits and Common Rosefinches, but the quietly gazing pigeon demanded attention. It had of course gone a little astray from its pigeon-house, ringed as it was and it seemed now to want to place its destiny in my hands. In the end it became a pencil drawing in my sketchbook and I remember my amazement over its seemingly strong desire of wanting to communicate with me.

That happened to me more than thirty years ago and the occasion is now brought to life. Most of us no doubt see domestic pigeons daily on streets and in marketplaces, or around farmyards in the country, without actually giving them any real attention. Perhaps we have been fascinated or worried by the huge numbers of them in London's Trafalgar Square or in the Piazza San Marco, in Venice. During salmonella outbreaks, or when the fear of bird-flu virus increased a decade or so ago, the domestic pigeon often became the object of negative discrimination. A not entirely uncommon comment is that they are 'flying rats'.

The domestic pigeon's aesthetics

From my kitchen window I look out over our garden and a gable on an outhouse which we use as a bicycle shed, woodshed and store for all manner of equipment and things which have been discarded. Doors and window-glass are, to say the least, leaky and ill-fitting and in some cases non-existent. On the upper floor the whole window frame fell out several years ago and Swallows now nest in there and, a few years back, domestic pigeons also did. When the pigeons perch on the window frame or the electricity cable, I am afraid that I associate them with all the droppings which I know are present there up in the loft. The constantly growing pyramids of dove dung which I see in front of me, hardly invite any thoughts on the species' conceivable aesthetic qualities. There is a very loose connection between everyday domestic pigeons and the white dove which, in Christian tradition, symbolises the Holy Ghost. It was in Luke 3:22 that God's spirit, in the form of a dove, flew from the sky and hovered above the waters of the river Jordan where Jesus was baptised. In the Old Testament, the dove's return to Noah with a laurel spray in its bill is a sign of peace between God and man. But all these doves are essentially Rock Doves which have been bred in endless forms over thousands of years.

If I am now ruining my relationship with the domestic pigeon, that makes me feel almost guilty. These are, after all, living birds and a part of the urban and agrarian ecosystem in which almost all of us are included. With a little reflection the Rock Dove is perhaps, in all its begotten forms, one of the most enthralling bird species that exists, from the historical perspective that is. Pigeons have, together with gallinaceous birds and wildfowl, been found in proximity of humans for a very long time.

How the domestication process came about hardly anybody knows, but one can imagine how it may perhaps have happened at the same time as the ox was tamed and the cultivation of wheat started in Mesopotamia, perhaps 10,000 or 12,000 years ago. Humans must have shared their habitations with Rock Doves ever since arriving from Africa. Wild doves could perhaps be caught in traps or the young be taken from rock ledges. Maybe this protein resource was already exploited by the modern human 50,000 years ago? The doves' breeding season was long, just as with many wild species. Perhaps they were transported alive as food and, if they got out of their cages, they flew back to their original cave or cliff and became a symbol – a sign which could be developed into a message, an announcement. Sending out pigeons from ships in order to ascertain the position of the nearest land was already described in the *Epic of Gilgamesh*, which takes place almost 4,000 years ago and has an obvious affinity with the story of Noah.

Carrier pigeons

Rock Doves are generally very site-faithful, a characteristic which led this species to be bred as a carrier pigeon. They can, in their attempts to find food, end up a long way from their colony during the day, only to return home with great precision towards the evening. This capacity has been engendered over thousands of years. Pigeons, as with many other birds, have several different ways of navigating. Their retina is able to distinguish polarised light and they can detect the earth's magnetic field by means of magnetic-sensitive cells in the inner ear. When they are approaching the pigeon loft or cliff they navigate by sight; it is therefore important that the pigeon house is visible in the landscape.

During the Middle Ages there was a sophisticated network of pigeon lofts to which pigeons were conveyed in cages by mules. The loft was a tower with a flat roof where a pigeon could land. Pigeons from different localities were kept in these pigeon lofts, or dovecotes. They were later released with a small sealed tube, often made of gold, containing a message which soon arrived at the pigeon loft which was that particular pigeon's home. During the carrier pigeons' heyday the pigeons were 'tattooed' on the white waxy cere at the base of the bill in order to guarantee that the mail came to the right address. According to the Egyptian historian al-Maqrizi (1364–1442), two thousand carrier pigeons were employed at the 'post office' in Cairo in 1288. Especially-fast pigeons, which could make longer trips, were bred in order to tie together, by letter, the larger cities' power centres. The tradition of racing pigeons, 'homing pigeons', which compete for which is the fastest, is, however, a more recent one. The sport was developed in Belgium and England at the beginning of the nineteenth century. These racing pigeons resemble mostly common domestic pigeons but have a pale swollen eyering, or orbital ring. As is also the case with horses, the most successful racing pigeons are the most highly coveted and can, in rare cases, fetch a price of more than two million Swedish kronor (more than £180,000/210,000 euros).

From an art-history perspective, doves and pigeons are probably depicted more than any other species. The picture of the domestic pigeon as a dove of peace is grossly misleading. Pigeons can go for each other with such frenzy that the outcome can be fatal. They are no more gentle in their territorial disputes than other birds are.

male

The domestic pigeon's habitat

The city's topography, with tower blocks and between them 'ravines' and 'dry stony plains', tallies well with the mountainous semidesert-like country that is the Rock Dove's main habitat. They are found also on cliffs along the European Atlantic coast and it was on the Faroe Islands that I, as a fifteen-year-old, saw Rock Doves for the first time. Well into the nineteenth century there was a population in southwest Norway in the region around Stavanger, centred on Rennesøy.

When I look at domestic pigeons, it is always the original colour form, the one which accords with wild Rock Doves, that can trigger a little ornithological curiosity. Down in the southernmost part of Gotland is a cliff, Hoburgen, where for so long as I can remember a small flock of domestic pigeons has nested in their original habitat. It was there that I suddenly started to become interested in their outward appearance.

The males have a considerably bigger area of shiny neck feathers, almost the entire neck being covered by such lustrous plumage. In poor light and in shadow, large parts of the neck can appear wholly dark and dull, but when the neck is ruffled up, or met by the light from a different angle, purple tones and emerald-green can develop. The females seen in direct comparison appear somewhat smaller and more moderate in neck iridescence. The area above the nostril is all white and more swollen than that of, for example, the Stock Dove. The bill is slightly thicker or more compact than the Stock Dove's and, not uncommonly, a white edge is formed on the lower mandible close to the bill base. The iris is often yellowish or orange with a darker red outer ring. The female's iris can often look duller. Young birds more frequently have a darker iris and some populations of Rock Doves look as if they have dark irides. Such is the case with all Rock Doves which I have studied in south Oman.

Here on Gotland, in spring, all three pigeon species can sometimes be seen foraging together on a newly sown field. They all walk in typical dove manner, with slightly jerky movements to and fro and gather up seeds. The domestic pigeon is, in size, somewhat smaller than the Wood Pigeon and clearly bigger than the Stock Dove. The original variant has a distinctly paler grey back colour than the others and a contrastingly darker blue-grey head. The two black bands across the wing are broad and sharply defined, whereas those of the Stock Dove are mostly a mere indication.

Tamduva
Hoburgsklippan 14.6.15
Kväll

WOOD PIGEON

Columba palumbus

THE WOOD PIGEON is the largest of the three grey pigeons. It looks obviously heavy, is long in the body and has a long tail. It is easily recognised by the white ring or patch on the side of the neck surrounded by mainly glossy green feathers. The feather structure above the neck patch appears extremely prominent on the adults and is reminiscent of dome-shaped series of fish scales or dense rows of sewn-on sequins. The shining pale iris, too, gives the bird an unmistakable facial expression. The pupil has been extended by a dark spot directed diagonally forwards and downwards and seems therefore not to be centred in the eye; the birds look a little cross-eyed and silly. Young birds lack the characteristic neck markings and on the ground can possibly be mistaken for one of the other pigeon species. The structure of the neck markings however, is already suggested in the first juvenile plumage.

Another character which is always decisive, is the large white transverse band running along the outer wing-coverts and which always gives away the species when on the wing. On the ground this feature is mostly concealed, though a white border along the lower edge of the wing is often visible; on the perched bird it is, in any case, not especially conspicuous. Wood Pigeons often breed late and it is not uncommon for a 'late-born' juvenile to turn up at the birdtable when the first snow arrives. These birds have not had time to moult in the neck patch and can create a little confusion for somebody who has seen only adult Wood Pigeons.

Alongside a Stock Dove the Wood Pigeon always looks bigger. The colour of the back verges more on brown, whereas the head has a colour that is purer blue-grey and the brownish-pink of the breast is more intense and runs farther down towards the belly. The impression therefore is that it is tricoloured, whereas the Stock Dove appears uniform in colour except for the iridescent neck patch. The Wood Pigeon's rump is weakly but perceptibly more bluish than the rest of the upperside.

The forest's timid pigeons

The Wood Pigeon is a common breeding bird over the greater part of Sweden, but occurs more sparsely in the interior of the north-central region and is absent from the mountain regions. In recent decades Wood Pigeons have begun to move into parks and gardens. In the mid-nineteenth century, in the north of Sweden, this species was a fairly shy forest bird, even though it did, like other pigeons, forage on open fields and meadows. When Erik Axel Karlfeldt wrote in *Fridolins visor* ('Fridolin's songs') in 1898 'the dove calls you to the darkness, where she laments', it was presumably the Wood Pigeon that gave its insistent calls from the depths of the spruce forest.

In 1848, Magnus von Wright, in *Finlands Foglar* ('Birds of Finland'), wrote that the Wood Pigeon resides in coniferous forest (preferably spruce forest) alongside the cultivated fields, which it visits during certain times of the day and is fairly shy. After Sweden entered the European Union, however, the Wood Pigeon's habits were harmonised with those of its continental conspecifics.

In supermarket freezers, the *skogsduva* (the Swedish name for the Stock Dove) is always the Wood Pigeon, as the word *skogsduva* (which, rather confusingly for the English reader, translates literally as 'wood pigeon') presumably sounds more 'gamebirdy' and appetising than *ringduva* ('ring dove', the Swedish name of the Wood Pigeon!). It is hunted commonly outside Sweden. There are an estimated one million pairs in Sweden and it has been steadily increasing in recent decades.

The Wood Pigeon is primarily a migrant, which, like the Stock Dove, moves down to France and Spain during the winter. The peak passage out of Sweden normally occurs in the first two weeks of October. Wood Pigeons have an extended breeding season and, not infrequently, nest late, and can still be feeding young into September. The numbers overwintering in Sweden, mainly in the south, change from year to year, depending mainly on the supply of beech mast. The Wood Pigeon is mostly a vegetarian, eating seeds, nuts and new shoots. Insects and other small animal items are rare in the diet. All pigeons are creatures of habit which often have specific routines. Wood Pigeons like to forage towards the evening and are seldom seen at feeding sites throughout the day, but generally one, or a small group, arrives during the late afternoon. A large part of the day is devoted to resting in a tree, however, late winter and spring and throughout the breeding period, they are often engaged in courtship in classic pigeon fashion. Wood Pigeons call with a deep and husky voice, a six-syllable slightly sluggish '*ho hoo ho hoho ho*'. The sound can easily remind one of an owl.

young Stock Dove
young Wood Pigeon
juvenil ringduva
med delvis nya
fjädrar
sen kull

The dove-grey colour

The Stock Dove was in the past often called the 'Blue Dove', which suggests that the species is seen as being more blue-toned compared with, for example, the Wood Pigeon, or perhaps better still, a domestic pigeon. In general, the Wood Pigeon is more brown-grey on the back while the domestic pigeon varies, but in its most original form the latter is palest and the most neutral grey of the three grey pigeons. When one studies a perched Stock Dove in the field, the rump is seen as being primarily a nice blue-grey. The pigeons' beautiful shades of grey induced me to investigate what the colour dove-grey, a word as attractive as it is elusive, actually represents. Both our perception of a given colour and how we describe it semantically have always had a degree of subjectivity. Our reference limits, or our palette of similes with regard to colours, also change over time.

The very words which describe different grey tones as steel-grey, smoke-grey, warm grey or ash-grey are likely to produce a broad spectrum of associations. But the material in itself, such as ash or steel, also presents images of properties in the surface which bears the colour. I believe that pigeons' plumage has a number of characteristics which give it, to our eyes, a special aesthetic quality. I have had the chance to study a dead Stock Dove and to compare the tints against a Natural Colour System (NCS) chart. The various finely tuned grey colour tones run invisibly into one another and the surface of the feathers feels dense and velvet-like. The eye's retina is sensitive to colour nuances and the way we see blue and red tinges in grey tones seems to be magnified by the brain. A neutral grey tone is seen as cold if we put something warm or reddish-grey near it, as if it had an element of blue in it. The majority of grey tones in lichens and stones have a warm tone and ash is more red-grey than blue-grey – at least if I test with my own birchwood ash from the stove and place it against various colour samples.

If you look in an art shop, you will no doubt be confronted with the colour chart Natural Colour System, or NCS. The chart is based on our visual perception of a colour, in which the darkness and the colour's saturation are given a number. It starts from the elementary colours, yellow Y, red R, blue B, green G together with black and white. From a circle with the four colour tints in their purest form at the four cardinal points, one can then select a shade such as mauve. A mixture of 50 per cent red and 50 per cent blue, then becomes 50R+50B, which can be simplified as R50B. Red comes before blue as the circle is read clockwise, from yellow in the north to red in the east and blue in the south. Since the total is always 100 per cent, it is sufficient to specify how much of one colour is included in the colour mix. If we now look for a colour which tends more towards blue, it can become instead 80 per cent blue and be written as R80B. We imagine a triangle with the bright tone at the top and the darkness scale from white to black at the base. A mid-grey tone which is entirely neutral ends up in the middle of the base, with 50 per cent black and 50 per cent white. Now we take away 5 per cent of the white colour and replace it with our blue tone which has a tinge of reddish and then we get black 50 per cent, colour 5 per cent and white 45 per cent. This can be written as 50+05+45 and then shortened to 5005. But in order to know which shade the colour tends towards, we add R50B and we get S5005-R50B, where S indicates that it is a standard colour within NCS. A neutral dark grey tone can then be S7000-N, where N stands for neutral, in other words it does not tend towards any colour tone.

When I attempt to check a Stock Dove's colour shades by actually comparing with a NCS scale, the paler grey parts of a Stock Dove, such as the rump or the outer wing-coverts, end up closest to S5005-R80B. The darker and comparatively more brown or neutral-toned scapulars are extremely close to a pure neutral tone with 70 per cent black S7000-N. There is no standard colour in NCS which has both red and blue in it and is lower in colour content than 5 per cent. Depending on the light and on how one makes the comparison, these figures can easily be raised in value of lightness by a tenth. I have however, decided that dove-blue or dove-grey is S5005-R80B on the basis of the rump of a Gotland Stock Dove which was killed by a vehicle in Hamra parish, in south Gotland, at some time in 2012.

von Wright's poppy-blue

Magnus von Wright uses the word poppy-blue for the 'beautiful blue-grey' colour which he ascribes to the Stock Dove, as well as to the Wood Pigeon. After having tried to find a poppy with this colour, I suddenly realised that he obviously had in mind the blue-grey variant

colour studies of Stock Dove

of the poppy seed, the little seeds which we occasionally get on small bread rolls. It is perhaps no coincidence that it was considered a relevant simile in the mid-nineteenth century, when opiates were much used in European medicine. It is poppy seed from the opium poppy *Papaver somniferum* that is found also in general use in bread-baking. The dried seeds, however, have a considerably milder effect than the latex from the unripe seed capsules. When I happen to see Stock Doves and Wood Pigeons foraging on the same field, I notice that the Wood Pigeon's head colour is a shade paler and has a smaller element of red. But perhaps this is only an optical illusion of the Wood Pigeon's upperparts as being more brown-grey or the breast being more intensely purple-toned. Maybe it is even the yellow eye that is playing a trick on me. Then there are the greyish tones which are mixed just with colour shades and the absolute truth is probably not to be found in any colour chart. Then, of course, the temperature of the natural light changes. Furthermore, my telescope lens has a coating which probably filters out a part of this light. I am therefore not going to protest if the word 'dove-grey' is used for the medium-grey shades of various pigeons, so long as we do not involve the Turtle Dove in this elusive *Columba*-grey complex.

Green and purple

One may well wonder why I am so interested in just the grey colour. The pigeons themselves seem to be attracted by the glossy iridescence of the neck. When the Stock Dove inflates its bellows, the sound is accompanied by this play of light, in green and in purple. Pigeons' feathers which have this quality are created by different structures of the keratin in the vane, the green colour being reflected only when it is seen from the front; when seen diagonally from the side, it is an underlying layer that reflects a purple colour. The colour often seems mysterious, as it is able to go from shining green to purple and can also change via a dark mixture of the same. The reverse is also found, with the purple colour uppermost and the green seen only from an angle. At close range the webs are seen to be thick and separated like hair. I assume that this characteristic, that the neck feathers can change colour and appear strongly iridescent, gives the grey colour an even more restrained beauty. The beauty in S5005-R80B – dove-grey.

STOCK DOVE

Columba oenas

IF THE DOMESTIC PIGEON does not produce any positive vibes among birdwatchers, the Stock Dove does so all the more. Most of us, I believe, think that the Stock Dove is the most interesting of the three grey *Columba* species – perhaps because it often nests in old Black Woodpecker holes, where Tengmalm's Owls also nest, or because it is somewhat more difficult to see, perhaps more gentle in its appearance, or expression. It is, moreover, a little less common than the Wood Pigeon.

The Stock Dove is smaller, shorter-tailed and more compact. Wood Pigeons always look more elongate. It looks generally uniformly soft grey or blue-grey, with a rudimentary dark bar on the inner greater wing-coverts and a pair of dark patches on the tertials (the innermost secondaries). The Stock Dove always has wholly dark eyes, which lends it its more gentle expression. Birds with 'black' eyes usually have a dark brown iris which appears black in the field and this applies to the Stock Dove. The reflecting iridescent green-and-purple neck patch is more restricted in extent compared with the domestic pigeon. The breast and foreneck are soft greyish red-mauve, the legs and feet raspberry-coloured. The bill is dull purple at the base, with the outer part pale yellowish-pink. The cere above the nostrils is bright white to a varying degree, probably more conspicuous in spring and on males. The young in its first juvenile plumage, is more dingy in colour and markedly insignificant; sometimes it lacks the distinct black wing markings altogether or these are smaller and less obvious, especially the rear two spots (on the tertials). The bill of immatures is flesh-coloured with a darker tip. In flight, the Stock Dove shows none of the Wood Pigeon's white markings, but on the wings there is an obvious lighter grey panel which can be somewhat surprising, as the perched bird looks uniformly grey. This character is most marked on the adults.

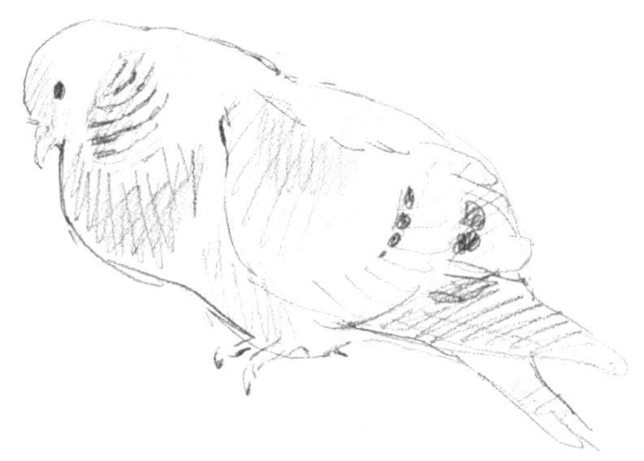

Occasional overwinterers

The Stock Dove is in fact a pronounced migrant which leaves Sweden during September and October for southwest France and northern Spain. However, occasional flocks may stop in southern Sweden over the winter at sites where food is present, in Scania often at properties where pheasants are fed. It sometimes winters farther north, but it is generally very uncommon during December and January in central Sweden. It is one of our earliest spring birds and can arrive back in Scania as early as the end of January. After a day of light southwest winds at the end of February, the first Stock Doves usually turn up in middle Sweden. It is also during late winter that the Stock Dove is in most cases reported at feeding stations.

It is then, too, that I myself get some of these lovely birds beneath my seed-dispenser. While the Wood Pigeons regularly visit feeding sites in spring, the Stock Doves are more infrequent visitors, this is despite the fact that the Stock Dove is a common bird in my part of the world. Occasional juveniles, which presumably hatched late and therefore stayed on in Sweden, do find their way to a feeding station.

The Stock Dove acquired its Swedish name *Skogsduva*, which means 'Wood Pigeon'(!), because it nests in trees. It is in fact no more tied to woodland than is the Wood Pigeon, but it requires cavities for nesting. On Gotland, Stock Doves often nest in stone mounds and stone walls and are therefore found in completely open pasturelands. They call with a soft disyllabic '*oo-oh*' repeated in shorter or longer series. The bird leans forward and seems to squeeze out the short syllables with the inflated neck acting as a bellows.

COLLARED DOVE

Streptopelia decaocto

THE COLLARED DOVE belongs to a different genus from that of the large grey doves and ornithologists use the scientific name *Streptopelia.* The Turtle Dove *Streptopelia turtur*, perhaps more discussed, also belongs to this genus. A 'streptopelia' is characterised by its smaller size and more elongate and slimmer body shape. The Collared Dove is a resident and the only one of its genus that occurs regularly at feeding stations in winter. An Asiatic species, the Oriental Turtle Dove *Streptopelia orientalis*, turns up as an extreme rarity at bird-feeders.

Like a face powder

The Collared Dove could perhaps be described as khaki-coloured, predominantly sandy or buff-grey. Against snow the colour can appear brownish-grey. There is, as with many pigeons, a peculiar pastel-like quality in its sublime colour tones, which gradually merge into one another. The head and neck, when seen at closer range, are old pink, the clarity of which decreases towards the breast, changing into a light grey colour which, on the undertail-coverts, darkens to 'dove-grey'. It has a fine whitish eyering and a blue-grey bill. The greater wing-coverts have a soft blue-grey tone on the outer part, a colour which is found again in the middle of the back. The whole bird can seem to appear generally 'beige', but it makes me think of a palette of face powder, dense warm soft colours. The only plumage feature that stands out is the blackish stripe across the neck side, its contrasting effect reinforced by a narrow white border. The iris is deep red, but often appears all dark in the field. In flight, when it rises from the ground, its nicely coloured tail, which is darker grey at the base and pale grey or greyish-white on the outer half except for the central feather pair, is conspicuous. The grey areas on the wing-coverts and back and the darker brown flight-feathers create a somewhat surprising effect of contrast. The underside of the tail reveals an even stronger contrast, a pattern which is demonstrated in the bird's flight display when it glides slowly with the tail partly spread. A couple of decades ago, when I had Collared Doves nesting in my garden, it was almost always the TV aerial that was the target for this advertising flight. They have, however, become more and more uncommon and nowadays I never see them in southern Gotland.

The Collared Dove has a three-syllable call, '*hu-huu hu*', which may be repeated in long series. This is something I often noticed as our aforementioned TV aerial was located right above our bedroom's skylight window and the doves began early with their courtship and called frequently through the protracted breeding season. The call is somewhat reminiscent of the Wood Pigeon's in tone, but has less depth in the voice and is clearly trisyllabic. The specific epithet *decaocto* means eighteen in Greek and that is indeed what the species is saying, in Latin. Collared Doves make themselves known also with a markedly hoarse '*ehhhh*', often given in flight as they approach a tree.

In Sweden the Collared Dove is known as *turkduvan*, the Turkish dove, referring to its immigration from the Middle East during the 1900s. The expansion from Turkey and the Balkans was associated with

huvud både rosa, grå
och beige
plommon i mjölk?
öga ser mörkt ut karminrött

the natural climatic change which occurred during the first half of the 1900s and it reached Scandinavia during the 1950s. During the 1960s the species very quickly turned up in a succession of places in Sweden. It established itself mainly in villages and towns and the number reached a peak in the 1970s and 1980s. The species has declined markedly in recent times but is still scattered in the southern half of the country and locally along the coast in the north. It breeds exclusively in parks and gardens.

In winter, the Collared Dove gathers in flocks around seed stores, larger farmyards and other places where there is food and regularly comes to feeding stations in areas where it is present. It feeds chiefly on various seeds, fruits and plant parts.

GREAT SPOTTED WOODPECKER

Dendrocopos major

IN WINTER, I OFTEN stand at the window and watch the regular visitors in their daily routines around the food site. When a Great Spotted Woodpecker turns up, quite often suddenly, it is always a bit of an event, a break in the routine. The smaller seed-eaters generally react to the fact that it is a bigger bird that is arriving; they become rather alert and some fly up into the nearest bush. One easily gets used to the more commonplace Great Tits, Tree Sparrows and Greenfinches, so the woodpecker's sudden arrival often provides a touch of splendour. There is something of the white shirt, black tail-coat and red patent-leather shoes in its appearance on stage. The woodpeckers' relative heaviness and specialised feet mean that when they first arrive they seldom land directly on the fatball or nut feeder. They are in the habit of first landing on a thickish trunk or branch nearby in order to assess the best way of approaching the food. If a bit of bacon rind has been nailed up or a suet bag suspended on a trunk, this is obviously the target. But if a nutbag or a fatball is involved, it seems that an hour of inner deliberation is needed over how the job should be done. Then it usually jumps forward as close as possible, approaches the target and clings beneath it. Hazelnuts in plastic nets are usually quickly opened and it may then take the whole nut and carry it away to some suitable trunk or strong branch for further treatment.

The facial expression when the woodpecker turns its head a little and, as it were, tries to work out how it should get to the food, provides the chance to see how attractive this bird actually is. It often has an expressive face, with a deep reddish-brown iris, a lovely beige forehead and often an almost blue-grey-bill. The female lacks the male's red square on the nape but otherwise looks exactly the same, with a bright crimson-red lower belly and vent. Certain individuals have snow-white underparts, but often an ochre or buffish tinge is visible on the belly and breast. I am convinced that this is resin staining from the substrate on which they have been climbing, perhaps resin from the wood inside the cavities in which they roost at night or on trunks which they have worked. The colour tone varies, some individuals having a strongly coloured underside whereas others are a dazzling white.

Moult

Juveniles leaving the nest hole have a wholly red crown and slightly more untidy markings on the scapulars and wings. Before winter arrives they moult into a plumage which is almost identical to that of the adults, but in some cases these immatures can be recognised. The simplest way is if one can identify the innermost, or in fact the second innermost, of the greater secondary coverts, which has been retained from the juvenile plumage. This is black and white, whereas the adults' corresponding feather is pure white. Beneath the rear part of the rectangular white scapular panel two narrow white patches are visible, which break the otherwise neat straight line against the black wing. I do not know if it always holds, but if a notch is visible there, this is a bird in its first winter.

This marking should not be confused with the bulging white area which is often formed by two or three of the innermost median coverts being white. These can be studied when the bird is perched at rest against the trunk after having eaten some suet.

Woodpeckers have a very particular moult which differs from that of most other birds. Even before they have left the nest hole they begin to moult the innermost primary and then continue to replace the rest one by one during the next three months. However, the secondaries are left unmoulted, as are the primary coverts and the inner greater secondary coverts. It is sometimes possible therefore to detect a hint of clearer black or brownish-black colour on these feathers, though this is often hard to discern unless the light is right. Usually it is the two white 'sugar lumps' on the second innermost greater secondary coverts that can be seen in the field.

young female
adult male

Generalist

The Great Spotted Woodpecker is the most common and numerous of all woodpeckers in north Europe and a common visitor to the birdtable. It nests generally in all landscapes where woodland or groups of trees are available. In Sweden it is absent only in the interior parts of the mountain tracts and it is calculated that there are more than 200,000 pairs in the country. For all those who feed birds and put suet, fatballs or nuts on the menu it is a familiar visitor, even if one lives in open country but has a garden with at least a few trees.

It feeds not only on insects and their timber-dwelling larvae but also on all kinds of seeds and nuts. It also takes eggs and chicks from bird nests during the breeding season. During the winter months, seeds from pine and spruce are the staple food. This means that the species occurs more numerously in most types of woodland. Anybody entering a wood containing an element of spruce or pine trees will often come across an accumulation of worked cones on the ground, which reveals that the Great Spotted Woodpecker has a 'workshop', or 'anvil', in the nearby tree. If one inspects some of the more peripheral and often dead parts of the tree towards the top, it is quite easy to locate this anvil: a well-worked area on some larger branch or on the trunk, which contains a crack or pecked-out cavity where the woodpecker wedges in the cone in order to work it. When it is firmly secured, it is worked with well-directed blows from slightly different angles until the seeds can be taken one by one. Often the bird needs to alter the position of the cone and it works a single cone systematically for several minutes. Before the cones open naturally in the spring or early summer, it is only the Great Spotted Woodpecker and the crossbills that are able to get the nutritious seeds out of their armoured casing. They prise away the cones directly from the branches and can look a little ungainly when climbing around in the top of a spruce. The cone is then transported in the bill to the anvil.

In some years when breeding has been very successful but the next seed set is likely to be poor, distinct southward migratory movements may be noted towards late summer. The species can then turn up in significant numbers on southern headlands, islands and other passage habitats. Numbers approaching 10,000 birds have been reported from certain sites in southern Finland.

Despite the fact that the Great Spotted Woodpecker is numerous, one often gets the feeling that there is only one or a pair at each feeding session. I often see a female and a male coming to my feeder, but hardly ever together; like all other woodpeckers, they seem to be solitary for the greater part of the year.

Short drumroll

The most common sound heard from the Great Spotted Woodpecker is a sharp ringing '*kick*' or '*keck*'. It can be uttered at slightly varying pitches, a little more vehemently as a warning call or simply what appears to be a genial communication in long series. When really agitated over something, it can emit a burst of chattering '*tchrett-cherr-cherr-cherr-cher*' in a voice sounding as if it still had a bit of suet stuck in the throat.

As with most woodpeckers, the male drums in spring in order to attract a female and to mark out its territory. The drumroll, which is produced by striking the bill on a dry branch, is short, ending within a second of starting. Not uncommonly a metal cover on a telephone pole is chosen, but usually it is a dead branch with a hollow that is selected as a sounding board. The other woodpeckers all have a more drawn-out roll.

male
Tail great spotted

Other pied woodpeckers

There are eleven species of woodpecker in Europe, plus one in North Africa which is a close relative of the Green Woodpecker. Of these, five species belong to the group known as pied woodpeckers, *Dendrocopos*, which all have a variegated pattern of black, white and red. They all readily exploit food put out in the form of, for example, lard, but it is only the Great Spotted and Lesser Spotted that occur regularly here on Gotland and which are treated in this book.

In the north there is also the very rare White-backed Woodpecker *Dendrocopos leucotos*. The wild population is almost extinct in Sweden but is present in small, sparse populations in southern Norway and locally in southeast Finland. It is more common in the Baltic Republics and east Europe. Attempts to reintroduce captive-bred individuals are in progress, with limited success. The species is more specialised in pecking out larger beetle larvae from decayed wood and it has been greatly disadvantaged by modern forestry practices. A few introduced individuals are present around the lower reaches of the Dalälven river in north Uppland. The chances of getting a visit from a White-backed Woodpecker are vanishingly small, but in winter 2013 a pair was seen at birdtables in Västerbotten and again in autumn 2015, several birds arrived over the Gulf of Bothnia from breeding sites farther east. Perhaps there is hope for the Swedish stock.

The Middle Spotted Woodpecker *Dendrocopos medius* is a smaller version of the Great Spotted with a wholly red crown and finely streaked underside. It bred in Östergötland, in southeast Sweden, up to 1982, but is not uncommon farther south in Europe. It appears to be expanding northwards and, very surprisingly, a female turned up on Gotland in December 2014 and stayed throughout the winter.

LESSER SPOTTED WOODPECKER

Dendrocopos minor

THE SMALLEST OF OUR WOODPECKERS is immediately recognised by its tiny size, being no bigger than a House Sparrow. It is rather uncommon on the whole but is also unobtrusive and does not make its presence known in the same way as the Great Spotted Woodpecker does. It prefers swampy woodland bordering streams or small rivers and shores where there are plenty of dead and dying broadleaf trees such as birch, alder and sallow. But it can also favour groups of trees in enclosed pastures and parks with older deciduous clumps. It even extends up into the mountain birch forest and it is only there that I have seen it visit birdtables. During one period we were often in Hemavan, in southern Lapland, in late winter/early spring. In addition to the more expected species at a birdtable in upland birch forest, such as Great Tit, Willow Tit, Bullfinch and Redpoll, newly arrived Snow Buntings and the Lesser Spotted Woodpecker came to visit. The Lesser Spotted Woodpecker seems to fit in best of all on birch trunks with much blackish cross-banding and lichens, where it merges in as if it were made out of the birch bark itself.

The juveniles' moult follows the same pattern as that of the Great Spotted Woodpecker; in other words, they retain the juvenile secondaries and greater primary coverts. Usually, however, they replace the greater secondary coverts. If a contrast is seen between browner and more worn primary coverts compared with newer and black primaries, this should indicate a bird in its first-winter plumage.

The Lesser Spotted Woodpecker feeds almost exclusively on insects and spiders. In winter it associates readily with tit flocks and forages to some extent in a similar manner, scrutinising every nook and cranny in bark, branches and lichen. A speciality which the Lesser Spotted Wood-

male
female

female

pecker has in common with the Blue Tit is its exploitation of common reeds in winter. The small body of these species enables them to perch horizontally on reed stems and slightly bigger plants. They then inspect the reeds to see if there are any lepidopteran larvae or pupae within them. A number of noctuid grass-moth species have chosen this habitation for the winter.

Drums hesitatingly

The call is a slightly piping '*ki-ki-ki-ki-ki-ki*'. The note often seems diminutive and the tempo can vary appreciably, it sometimes sounding as if the call is being squeezed out against some resistance: '*pyip pyip pyip pyip-pyip-pyip-pyip*'. In addition, occasional '*kick*' calls are given, as with the Great Spotted Woodpecker.

The drumroll is normally distinctly drawn out, almost two seconds long and tends to begin a little tentatively and then drop in the middle before continuing. It has a more rattling tone compared with the Great Spotted's hollow echoing tone. Sometimes it gives just the first half and the woodpecker seems to want to begin once again in order to get to the long rattling series. The sound carries for a much shorter distance than that of its larger relative, but it can sometimes be difficult to judge the distance of a drumming woodpecker.

male

GREEN WOODPECKER

Picus viridis

THE TWO 'GREEN WOODPECKERS' are closely related to each other and exhibit the same range of colours. The Green Woodpecker is clearly bigger and looks somewhat disproportionate in comparison with the more slender Grey-headed Woodpecker; the head and bill are larger, giving a more front-heavy impression. The back colour is somewhat brighter and more warm green and, in sunlight, it can really glisten just like young aspen leaves. The colour of the head and underparts is also more greenish-grey and more richly coloured than the Grey-headed Woodpecker. The rump has a golden lustre which appears almost luminous when the bird flies. The rump feathers are different in structure, as if frayed, which presumably brings out the brilliance of the colour.

Possible identification problems in relation to the Grey-headed Woodpecker disappear if one looks closely at its face, as the two have completely different expressions. Pasted on its face the Green Woodpecker has a large black-and-red 'marimekko' flower out of which a whitish button-like eye stares irascibly. As with the Black Woodpecker, there is a black pigmentation around the pupil and this gives the Green Woodpecker a markedly staring eye, a little reptile-like and vacant.

Both sexes have a long silky red crown but only the male has a red centre in the black moustachial stripe, such that one can easily tell the female from the male. When the juveniles appear in early summer they are heavily pale-spotted above and dark-spotted below and on the head. They lack the adults' black bandit's mask but have already developed the sexual differences regarding the moustachial stripe, all black on the female, the male with red. The secondaries from the juvenile plumage are retained through the winter and until the next year's complete moult. This often enables immatures to be distinguished by their having small pale speckles or stars towards the tips of the inner three secondaries, the tertials. They also tend to have more contrasting barring on the inner webs. The greater primary coverts, which are also retained, are likewise more contrastingly marked than those of the adults.

The two species belong to a group of woodpeckers which are sometimes called 'ground woodpeckers' and therein lies the explanation of why they are predominantly green on the upperparts. They feed largely on ants which they find on the ground, down beneath turves or in ant-hills. Against the grass surface the colour functions as a camouflage. They have a very long tongue, about ten centimetres, with which they can investigate ant runs in search of eggs, larvae and pupae. The tongue has a sticky secretion and the outer part can be moved like a long finger into the runs. Several of the species which the Green Woodpecker often eats, such as yellow and black lawn ants, occur in large numbers in cultivated terrain; the Green Woodpecker is therefore common in arable farmland where scattered trees and clumps of trees alternate with gardens and grazed grasslands. It avoids overly dense woodland and requires a strong element of deciduous trees in order to thrive. In woodlands the red wood ant is a common food. In winter the bird can use its relatively large bill to shovel its way down to ant communities beneath the snow and its ravages are often noticed where it is common. The Green Woodpecker digs out its nest hole in a thickish tree trunk, often an aspen, but rarely forages in trees, or digs for insects in dead wood.

The species is principally a rarity at the birdtable, only exceptionally visiting suspended fat or suetballs. The ground near a feeding site can, however, create a better microclimate for various insects and often is kept snow-free, so it can attract a Green Woodpecker during cold and snowy winters.

Uncommon in the north

The Green Woodpecker is common in south and central Sweden but becomes gradually more uncommon north of the Dal River (Dalälven), in north Uppland, though its range reaches north to Medelpad, more than halfway up the east coast of Sweden. The Green Woodpecker was probably more numerous in Sweden during the mid-twentieth century, the population having diminished appreciably from the 1970s up to the

female

1990s. Thereafter its numbers stabilised. Whether this was due to the reduced livestock-farming and the resurgence of light wooded pastures during the period or to the harsh winters during the 1970s and 1980s is not known, perhaps a combination of the two. Many of the lawn ants, which are an important food source, benefit from the ground surface being grazed. The number of Green Woodpecker pairs in Sweden is estimated at 18,000. This is a species whose distribution is largely restricted to Europe west of the River Volga. One arm of its range, however, extends across Turkey, the Caucasus and in a narrow band along the southern shore of the Caspian Sea. Isolation in various climatic epochs during the Pleistocene has periodically separated certain populations in the south and a few different colour variants have evolved. In North Africa there is one such isolated population which is now given its own species status, Levaillant's Woodpecker *Picus vaillantii*.

Green Woodpecker

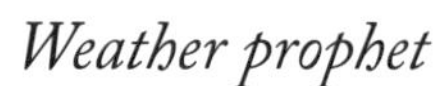

Weather prophet

In popular belief, woodpeckers have been regarded as being able to predict the weather and it was thought, in particular, that their calls foretold rain. Sven Nilsson, in his 1858 book on Scandinavian fauna, wrote that 'an eminent meteorologist assured me that the Green Woodpecker proclaims the weather around three days in advance. If he gives a low monotone call, the weather will be nice; if he screams loudly, there will be rain and bad weather; if he comes close to the house and screams, it will be even worse.'

The Green Woodpecker's spring call has a somewhat plaintive tone, a melancholy series of nasal '*kleu-kleu-kleu-kleu-kleu-kleu-kleu*' which is often delivered from a lookout point at the top of a solitary aspen or oak. In its form it can perhaps be reminiscent of the gurgling sound from a bottle when one empties out its contents: 'kleug-kleug…'. The rhythm or the speed varies as does the shrillness and the call is given by both sexes. The Green Woodpecker also utters a few nasal '*kyah*' notes, not unlike a hoarse Jackdaw but more forced. Often these are given in a slightly untidy series, '*kyah kya-kya-kya-kya*', which is the sound most often heard during the autumn and winter. If the birds are agitated or warning others, this series can become more forced or cracked in tone. Whether there are differences in the pitch of the spring 'song' or in the call and warning cry which are said to enable determination of the weather I do not know. In any case, we are dealing with both male and female fortune-tellers out in the woodlands of south and central Sweden. They rarely drum and then only weakly and feebly.

Green-and-golden bird

In Sweden this woodpecker's name is *gröngöling*, *grön* meaning 'green' and *göling* probably being a synonym of *gyllene*, meaning 'golden'. This alludes to the brilliant golden-coloured rump, and the name 'gröngylling' (green-and-golden being) has frequently been used in the past. But it is possibly instead a verbal noun from the word *göla*, to splash in water, alluding to the Green Woodpecker's ability to foretell rain.

Grey-headed Woodpecker

For most people who are not particularly interested in birds, the Swedish word *gröngöling* is a synonym of the word *nybörjare*, meaning 'novice' or 'tyro', for which the English word 'greenhorn' is an equivalent. My own first impression of the Green Woodpecker was when I was perhaps six or seven years old and for a couple of weeks lay every day under a big aspen and watched a pair of these birds as they chiselled out their nest hole. I recall a feeling of bliss when the wood splinters landed on me where I lay at the base of the tree. At the time, the *Kalle Anka* (Donald Duck) comic in the letterbox was otherwise the big event on Fridays. And if his nephews *Knatte*, *Fnatte* and *Tjatte* (Huey, Dewey and Louie) put on their green woodpecker shirts that meant excursions out in the woods and fields, even more exciting. When I later became a wolf cub in the scouts, there was a certain disappointment that we did not become Green Woodpeckers. Here on Gotland there are no Green Woodpeckers and on the rare occasions nowadays when I hear their spring call, it awakens childhood memories from the southern suburbs of Stockholm.

I did many Green Woodpecker paintings at that time and I still have some of these. The neck and the back of the head of the Green Woodpecker have a pastel-like greenish-grey colour which corresponded exactly with the tint of one of my oil-pastel crayons, I think it was olive-green, or maybe olive-grey. On the back I have made the colour far too bright green; but the neck was given the right colour, like the underside of an olive leaf, pastel-grey with a slight tinge of green.

GREY-HEADED WOODPECKER

Picus canus

THE GREY-HEADED WOODPECKER is not so colourful as the Green Woodpecker. Its tones are more moderate and the whole bird seems as if it was telling us that we have now been transported from the deciduous woods of south-central Sweden up to the forests and clearings of Hälsingland. The facial markings in particular are very different from those of the Green Woodpecker. The dominant colour on the head is grey, the moustachial stripe is narrow and only the male has a red crown, the female being plain-faced. The bill is much weaker and the whole bird appears more subdued, more balanced. The expression is slightly odd; the iris is to a varying degree pale, but the bird always looks red-eyed as if from long nights at the charcoal kiln. It has a distinct 'undershot jaw', or it gives that impression as the throat feathers extend well out under the bill. Only at certain angles does the male's gleaming red sports cap show and often it is barely visible. The rump and lower back are lighter greenish-yellow but do not shine in the same way as those of the Green Woodpecker do. When an individual flies, it is obvious that the species is smaller and lighter, with a more spool-shaped body.

The aspen's bark

When I was sitting in my Gotland studio at the beginning of June and had to conjure up a feeling of presence for the species, I searched among all manner of different photographs in old journals and, of course, on the internet. The Grey-headed Woodpecker is a regular visitor to suet and is likely the most frequent woodpecker at feeding stations after the Great Spotted. So, there are lots of good Grey-headed Woodpecker pictures to study.

Earlier in the year I searched for the species at well-known breeding sites in north Uppland, but this resulted only in calls from distant birds and brief impressions from flying birds. My sketchbook remained empty. Then I sat with some older pencil sketches from the same region. Artist's dilemmas soon presented themselves: is it as green as a Green Woodpecker, is the tone as warm, as greenish-yellow, as bright? This kind of fine-tuned assessment is hard to determine on photographs.

In the end I went out into the wood to a place where I know that there are some well-grown aspen trees which could at least provide inspiration for the background. I thought of this woodpecker as being greenish-grey like aspen bark. Inside the wood the meadowsweet stood tall, the mosquitoes were hungry for warm blood and the Wren sang in competition with the Song Thrushes. I found that some of the large aspens had recently been felled and sawn into two-metre lengths. After I had sat and painted for an hour the mosquitoes became too much for me.

I carried back to my studio, with some difficulty, a thick branch supplemented with slightly thinner fresh branches. Now I could look at its structure and colour in greater detail, and I discovered that the aspen's surface depicted not only the Grey-headed Woodpecker's various colour tones but also its external structures. The neutral grey lichens with varying areas of paleness, their rough surface replicated the tract around the corners of the bill, even the sharp black markings. There the bark gave the green tones, the lichens all the grey and yellowish tinges and the branches' annual shoots the cold reddish-purple colour of the eye. The contrasting barring on the primaries was created by the outer branches' distinct growth segments as slightly glossy reflected light in a regular pattern – all was found there, painted on the surface of the aspen bark. Is it the case that the Green Woodpecker imitates the early-summer grass on the ground whereas the Grey-headed Woodpecker has developed its colour so as to be wholly camouflaged against the aspen bark? Who knows, but the thought struck me. Evolution is an eye of the needle which generation after generation must go through. The Grey-headed Woodpecker prefers to sit in an aspen and watch the ground for ants.

Hälsingland's woodpecker

When I started work on my bird guides in the early 1970s, the Grey-headed Woodpecker was a rarity, an enigmatic bird which few were thought to have seen well and at close range. The entire Swedish population then was estimated at 200 pairs. When I finally got to see my first Grey-headed Woodpecker, perched far off in a solitary aspen tree in a clearing, I had a feeling of having undergone an initiation rite. I had ticked Grey-headed Woodpecker and was therewith initiated into a deeper understanding of the essence of birdwatching. Since then the species has increased in numbers and can be quite easily sought out by anybody wanting to get to know it better. Perhaps it has been favoured by the fact that the forestry companies, to a greater extent, allow occasional deciduous trees to remain standing in the clearings and that clearings themselves favour the presence of certain ant species.

The current population in Sweden is relatively small, about 2,000 pairs; there are a hundred Great Spotted and ten Green Woodpeckers for every Grey-headed Woodpecker throughout the country. On Gotland it is, like the Green Woodpecker, entirely absent. The distribution from central Europe eastwards all the way to the Pacific Ocean follows a belt along the southern part of the taiga, where a mixture of coniferous and deciduous trees creates an optimal habitat. In Sweden it is found north of the Dal River (Dalälven), with a centre in Hälsingland.

In central Europe however, the Grey-headed Woodpecker is found also in pure deciduous woodland and in many places breeds side by side with the Green Woodecker. Rarely, hybrids between the two species occur, these having been documented at least in Poland. It has a liking for more open zones with occasional solitary deciduous trees, preferring aspen and birch. Far away in Asia the Grey-headed Woodpecker's distribution also extends down into pure tropical regions and a number of races have evolved which in some cases look completely different from the Grey-headed Woodpecker which follows the aspen's distribution. It is evident that the Grey-headed Woodpecker was isolated from the Green Woodpecker in the east and expanded from there during the present warm period, the Holocene. While the Green Woodpecker has developed various isolated populations in the southwest Palearctic, the Grey-headed Woodpecker has done the same in southeast Asia. The image of the Grey-headed Woodpecker as a forest troll from Hälsingland is a qualified truth.

Drop in tempo and tone

Like the Green Woodpecker, the Grey-headed calls from various strategic places within its territory. The tone is weaker and more squeaky and towards the end it usually drops in tempo and pitch as if it did not have quite enough air left to complete the phrase, '*pi-pi-pi-pi pi pu pu pu puh*'. The Grey-headed Woodpecker drums more regularly than the Green Woodpecker, the roll being fast and relatively long, almost a couple of seconds, but sounds more like a vibration than a drumroll. Other contact and anxiety calls are reminiscent of the Green Woodpecker's but weaker and perhaps more clipped in nature, '*kyik, kyik, kyik, kyik*' or single '*kyik*' notes.

BLACK WOODPECKER

Dryocopus martius

THE BIGGEST OF THE EUROPEAN WOODPECKERS, as big as a crow. Long and slender and sooty black, the male has a red crown and the female a red skull-cap on the rear crown. The bill is ivory-coloured and the iris dirty white. An unwritten rule with woodpeckers is that the bigger they are, the more foolish they look. Conversely, it holds that the smaller they are, the more cute their expressions are. The Black Woodpecker always looks imposing with its size and bearing, but it also gives a somewhat disproportionate impression and it looks a little deformed with its long slender neck and its powerful and angular rear head. The whitish iris has black pigmented spots next to the pupil, making it appear a little cross-eyed. It looks quite simply somewhat comical, as if it were a caricature of itself. It is not by chance that woodpeckers got to play the role of half-mad types in Walt Disney's role-casting.

The Black Woodpecker has been presented with long trousers. It has black feathering right down to the foot, which makes me think of old-fashioned black ski-trousers, those which narrowed downwards and were fastened under the sole of the foot with a piece of elastic. If you do not remember, have a look at an old James Bond film!

Flappy flight

If one comes across a Black Woodpecker in the forest it is often sitting on a stump, very close to, or at the base of, a tree. Perhaps it retreats a little behind the trunk with a scraping sound from the big claws. If one deliberately tries to approach it, it can become a little suspicious and hide itself from the observer. Sooner or later it peeps out from behind the trunk or the stump. In flight, which is often high above the forest, the course is straight but the bird looks slightly unsteady, with broad cranking wings and a big upward-tending bill. Even though the Nutcracker is a rare bird, it is the species which one first thinks of when a Black Woodpecker passes across a clearing or from one wood to another.

A Black Woodpecker on a winter visit

In the southernmost part of Gotland, what we call Storsudret, a peninsula joined to the main island by a broad isthmus, there was once a small population of Black Woodpeckers, but they disappeared a couple of decades ago. When we look back on it, their disappearance was sudden and I saw no Black Woodpecker in my neighbourhood for at least 15 years. I do not have any more detailed notes on when I saw the last one here, but its disappearance was nevertheless obvious. In the middle of Storsudret there is more or less unbroken pine forest over at least a few thousand hectares which could well support several pairs of Black Woodpeckers and the species is otherwise not uncommon on Gotland.

One snowy winter a few years ago, a female turned up suddenly around my studio. The studio is situated near the coast in a relatively open arable landscape where farms with their own group of deciduous trees follow one after the other, with one or two fields in between. My group of trees was perhaps one hectare in size, mostly with valuable broadleaf deciduous species such as oaks, maples and limes, but also a number of birches which had died from unknown causes, probably drought. I had seen them slowly degenerate until they finally started to collapse. It looked untidy and I felt a little ambivalent, whether I should try to take them away or whether they should be allowed to lie there. The feeling was overwhelming when, one late-autumn day, I heard a long rolling '*prii prii prii...*' so loud and characteristic that it could not be missed – a Black Woodpecker had arrived. It had discovered that my grove of trees had the right timber.

It took a few days before I caught sight of it, a female with just a red kippah on the back of the head. In that winter I had the telescope set up by the window and a sketchpad in place so that, as soon as I heard or saw something, I would be ready to direct the telescope on her. Then she visited me regularly and worked the roots of all of my fallen birches

female

throughout the winter, until she disappeared at some time in March.

The effect that Black Woodpeckers have is quite incredible. Several of the large thick birches were pulverised at the roots one after another and it is easy to understand that it requires rather large areas and plenty of half-decayed timber if a pair of Black Woodpeckers is to have sufficient employment for a season. The principal prey item is carpenter ants which live inside rotting tree stumps. These ants are seldom seen as they are nocturnal, but they are the reason why Black Woodpeckers tackle, with intensity and assiduousness, just the lower metre or so of trees which have passed their 'best-before date'. There was plenty of snow that winter, but the female easily shovelled away the snow with sweeping movements of her large head. Black Woodpeckers consume other ants too, besides beetles and beetle larvae. I once saw two Black Woodpeckers in mid-summer clambering around in a cherry tree to eat the red drupes.

The Black Woodpecker prefers older thick-stemmed pine forest or mixed forest, but occurs also in pure deciduous woodland. It is relatively common, but pairs are thinly distributed over most of Sweden except in the mountain regions. The fact that it is found on Gotland reveals that it is a partial migrant in some years or leads a nomadic existence. It seems that the species may vary in numbers cyclically. The number of pairs in Sweden is estimated at almost 30,000. A large proportion of Gotland's ash trees was severely threatened by the fungus *Chalara fraxinea* during the early years of the present century and many have slowly died since then. This is possibly the reason why the Black Woodpecker has returned to the Storsudret.

Sounds like a sea-eagle

The male's call is not unlike a Green Woodpecker's in form, a series of cries with a slightly melancholy but less nasal tone, '*kli-kli-kli-kli-kli-kli-kli*'. I have more than once taken the sound for the call of a White-tailed Eagle, as it is somewhat raptor-like in the way it is squeezed out and has a vacillating rhythm. In flight and especially on arriving at the nest, it gives the characteristic rolling flight call, which is very loud. When it drops down into a tree, a drawn-out slightly metallic mewing '*klee-ay*' is heard, a call which, according to Gotland folklore, foretells rain. Woodpeckers have always been considered to be weather prophets in popular belief and it can sometimes be hard to keep track of whether it is the Black Woodpecker or the Green Woodpecker that announces rain, or maybe it is both. Their songs are not entirely different from each other and I am not really sure whether interpreters of the woodpeckers' predictions in those days could tell the species apart. The drumroll is characteristic in its powerfulness and duration. It is audible at great distance, often a couple of kilometres and has a straight and even pitch. It sounds as if the Black Woodpecker has wound up the spring to the maximum before planting its bill on the timber, the thunderous noise sounding like a distant machine-gun salvo.

WAXWING

Bombycilla garrulus

THE WAXWING breeds in the taiga. In Norrbotten, in the far north of Sweden, where it has its stronghold in the country, it is most common in the north and up to the forests near the mountains. It readily breeds in older coniferous forest, often slightly swampy spruce forest mixed with birch, beside bogs, small rivers and rivulets. In summer it is a fly-catcher which elegantly takes midges and damselflies in the air. This habit can be seen on calm early-spring days in the south when the first insects are in flight, or on still November days when autumn has hung on. It is long-winged and short-legged like a true flycatcher and extremely fast in flight. It could be compared with the bee-eaters of the south, which perch on the look-out and make rapid raids on flying insects.

Painter from the north

The Waxwing's plumage depicts its northern landscape. A thousand shades of grey in lichens, birch trunks and spruce branches are set against the deep rusty-red crowberry shrubs. The black bog water provides sharp relief against yellow marsh marigolds and white cotton-grass, the wax-like protuberances like red whortleberries. For those who have grown up in central Sweden, in my case in a suburb of Stockholm, the nomadic flocks are a sign that the autumn is going over into winter. With a little imagination I can also see my own suburban-landscape colour palette against a grey November sky – the pastel tones in greyish-pink and brownish-buff on sprayed frontages of 1950s three-storey houses, rowanberries and the streets' yellow warning signs in place of the spring's marsh marigolds. Perhaps all the grey tints depict the sky at dusk where the city's different lights are reflected. Many people encounter the silvery calls of flocks from the north in the ornamental apple trees and rowans along avenues or in supermarket car parks. Just as the Twite and the Snow Bunting are now the heralds of winter along my shores in November, I recall with warmth the first Waxwings which came to the Stockholm suburb of Hökarängen, just as autumn turned towards winter. The thin ringing call is like frost crystals, silvery and it always makes me look towards the sky. Either it is a flock moving quickly across the sky, or else the whole flock is perched at the top of a leafless tree and making joint sallies towards a berry-bearing bush or tree. Their abilities as acrobatic fly-catchers are just what is needed in the raids for berries. With short legs and an ability to hover they can reach the berries on the outermost twigs and they swallow them whole at a rapid rate. The sight of a dense flock of Waxwings at work in berry-filled branches is magnificent, almost unreal, like a flock of parrots in a tropical fig tree, but with a northern colour scale. If disturbed in any way the whole flock takes off, then they all dive down towards the berries again or move away to some other neighbourhood.

Of course, Waxwings come to my Gotland countryside too. The first arrive around mid-October, but it is not until the end of that month and early November that they are usually seen more regularly. The flocks are often restless and seldom so confident as those in cities and towns. Out in the country they seek out Swedish whitebeam and rowan trees so long as these are still bearing fruit and then rose hips and juniper berries. Apples and pears are naturally taken with great relish. Not uncommonly they perch on the ground and consume fallen berries. They do however, move quickly through the landscape and disappear as suddenly as they turned up. Trees and bushes in the towns and suburbs are often loaded with fruit and can host flocks for a longer period. Adaptation to the rich autumn fruit feast where fermented berries are often on the menu has generated a special ability to break down alcohol. Their liver is able to accept four times more than the human liver can. Despite that, they not uncommonly become intoxicated and within towns and cities are frequent victims of traffic, cats or reflective window panes. In older times these Waxwings were welcomed edible birds at the dining-table, so easy were they to catch.

In big invasion years the flocks reach far south on the continent and across to Britain. The return migration through southern Sweden, if they have left the country at all, occurs in the latter part of March and in April, then rarely in larger flocks but only in smaller groups. They come to the birdtable preferably if apples, pears or other fruits are there.

adult male

young female
young male

Increasing numbers

The number of Waxwings breeding in Sweden has increased, but the variations from one year to another are considerable. There is no definitive or simple explanation for why they are numerous in some years and few in others. Waxwings in the north are breeding at the extremity of their range and numbers are governed by several factors; possibly there are underlying natural cycles, too. In years when they have wintered in good numbers in western Europe, one can imagine that some will breed here in the following spring. The population can build up slowly to a peak and, if this coincides with a poor berry year, mass emigration can take place. During the summer they feed also on bilberries, cowberries (lingon) and other woodland berries in the ground layer. When we see large numbers of Waxwings in Sweden it is highly likely that many of these come from the east. In the Swedish bird atlas of 1999, the authors emphasised that the species is very hard to census. A guess at the Swedish breeding population then was that the figure was probably between 1,000 and 50,000 pairs. In the latest edition (2012) of *Fåglarna i Sverige* the population was estimated at 80,000 pairs.

Age differences

If one studies a flock of Waxwings, one quite soon sees that they vary somewhat in wing markings. The variation is between males and females, as well as between immatures and adults. In wing characteristics, however, there is overlap between females and younger males. Older males have broad strong yellow outer edges on the primaries apart from the two visible outermost ones and they have a broad white border which encloses and clearly accentuates the tips of the feathers. The secondaries have several, longer and broader wax-like red appendages. Young females have only a narrower white border along the primaries and no marking at the tip, thus presenting a more moderate range of colours. Older females, like young males, have a yellow edging on the primaries, but lack white at the tips or may have a thinner white rear edge or a mere suggestion of it. Some individuals also have thin reddish quills protruding on the yellow tip of the tail feathers, this being more

common on older males. Sometimes autumn flocks contain a solitary partly-juvenile bird, which has not completed the moult into its first adult plumage. Such birds immediately cause surprise because of their different and colourless face and the fact that they lack a crest and have grey spots running down the breast. On young birds (first winter) the dark bib is duller black and merges smudgily into the breast. However, when you watch a flock in the field busily eating berries, it is primarily the wing-feather markings that you are able to observe and assess.

Painting the silk colour

It is frequently difficult to describe how individual birds' colours, colour transitions and general material feel are interpreted. The Waxwing's exquisitely beautiful plumage has some effect on most people who observe it. In water colours I have many times struggled to get the colour to reflect the inner experience I have, the feeling which the bird creates. I work wet on wet in order to create the soft tonal transitions. If two different colour tones with the same water content meet, the water blends these into a perfectly soft transition. Often I add a little zinc-white gouache colour in order to make the hue slightly softer, more pastel-like in character. When I paint Waxwings with their many small transitions, almost always a sharper unwanted border is formed which compels me to set to afresh with the brush, just a little. Then the magic is broken, the weightless transition and I begin to work the surface mechanically so as to get back to where I was. It needs more and more covering layers of paint and the air among the feathers disappears – it becomes more of a gouache painting instead. Oil colour is better suited for this; it can be mixed softly, all the time until the linseed oil has started to congeal, while watercolour only becomes more awkward the more it is worked.

Sven Nilsson was also fascinated by this bird's lovely plumage. He wrote that the Waxwing is one of Europe's most beautiful birds, the whole plumage soft, silky and fairly bushy. His contemporary, Magnus von Wright, took great pains to try to describe the Waxwing's colour tones and soft transitions in colour: he noted that the breast has a markedly attractive reddish-grey colour which passes into various tints and ends in the almost whitish-grey belly which at its lowermost point has a strong coating of pale ochre-yellow. The weak yellow tone is hardly ever seen in the field, but on some individuals it may be discerned on the lowermost belly. Von Wright's fascination with the subtle smooth colour transitions on the underparts he summarises with the words: 'All these colours are particularly pleasing in the way they merge into one another. At a quick glance the underside can seem to be uniformly greyish-pink or greyish-buff. The colour reddish-grey, if it is present at all, does, however, capture well the depth of this colour. Between red and grey there exists a sky and a forest of hues. And a whole lifetime of interpretations.'

DUNNOCK

Prunella modularis

AN ANONYMOUS SPECIES IN SWEDISH BIRDLIFE, of common occurrence but unknown to most people. The size of a Tree Sparrow, it presents a generally dark overall impression. Above, it is warm brown with darker feather edges and with a distinctive blue-grey colour on the head and breast. The sexes are alike, but the males have a purer grey colour, a brighter more rusty-brown upperside, are less streaked on the breast sides and have a brownish-red iris. Females in their first winter can sometimes have a colour pattern that is very cryptic, more uniformly striped grey and brown and with a paler grey-brown iris. The paler spots, or milia, under the eye are characteristic. The bill is, perhaps mainly on juveniles in autumn, pale flesh-coloured at the very base.

The Dunnock is a migrant in Sweden, leaving the country in September–October for southwest Europe. A few attempt to overwinter after mild autumns. They return at the end of March, at the same time as the passage of Robins, Song Thrushes and Chaffinches reaches a peak. It is then that I regularly get Dunnocks visiting my feeding station. The fine, pointed bill gives away their diet of insects and spiders. They have a low body carriage and hop close to the ground, fliping and turning over leaves and plant material to find food. They come to the birdtable mainly if the ground freezes and becomes snow-covered, but they are seen regularly in small numbers, chiefly in the most southerly regions. They then consume bits of suet and seeds which have fallen to the ground.

In the north, the Dunnock breeds in bushy woodland, often in clearings with young spruce growth, but also in pure shrubbery and in gardens. It is unobtrusive in winter, usually giving a drawn-out clear '*siiih*'. On migration a fine three-syllable '*si-si-si*' is commonly heard. Males sing in spring from a low lookout, a clear shuttling series, like the Wren's but at lower speed.

male
young female winter

WREN

Troglodytes troglodytes

THE WREN is one of our smallest bird species and thrives among dense and brushy vegetation with many small arthropods. In the north it is a pronounced forest bird which makes its presence known mainly by its loud and lively song. Anybody visiting woodland will often come across it near a root pile or a heap of brushwood from an old felling operation. First a few hard short '*tek tek*' notes are heard and then perhaps you see a small brown ball fly away at knee height. One rarely has time even to notice that there was something speeding away before it has disappeared, much as one may see a mouse running away indoors. Rarely is there time to see any wingbeats. It has a liking for brushy and complex micro-habitats where it can find narrow spaces which harbour insects, mainly small beetles and spiders. That is why we quite often come across it in gardens with brushwood and piles of leaves, in wood stacks or by stone walls and thickets. It does not actually come to birdtables, but is, like the Treecreeper, readily drawn to roving tit flocks. In exceptional cases it eats berries and fruits, but I have never observed it to eat from the birdtable. Its movements are quick and slightly jerky, but sometimes it moves up on to a suitable lookout post and stops for a moment. When you have had a proper view of the bird it can hardly be mistaken for anything else: rounded and ball-like, large-headed and with shortened stern where the tail is usually cocked like a little peg over the back. The Dunnock may on a fleeting view give a similar dark brown impression, but it always appears bigger. The Wren looks a little stern despite its small size and one would like to give it the epithet 'tough'. The colour is warm brown on the back with a fine vermiculation which becomes

more intense across the wing and merges into a fine barring on the flight-feathers. It has a distinctly long supercilium which reinforces the somewhat irascible facial expression.

Loud song

The Wren gives away its presence by its loud noisy calls, '*tek tek*' or '*trett trett*', which are often repeated in a rapid staccato, a very dry rattle. The name Wren comes from the word 'wrench', an adjustable spanner or screwdriver and the staccato sounds roughly like a mechanical twisting moment, or torque, from an old wooden screw. That it is a little midget that is twisting the screw becomes apparent when it suddenly pops up. Birds which have established winter territories may sing as early as autumn and during the winter, but they sing most intensively during the breeding season in spring and early summer. The song makes me think of the bird sounds which can be heard now and then from some shop in pedestrian areas of cities. A long and heated series of high trilling notes which quickly change into syllables. It is very loud and anybody who does not know that the bird is so small can be amazed if the songster reveals itself.

Overwinterer

The Wren can increase in numbers after a series of mild winters and then seems to be present everywhere in the wood, only to disappear almost completely after one hard winter. Many are on their way south during the autumn, mainly in September and October, but a large part of the population will attempt to overwinter in south and central Sweden. It belongs to a genus which originated in America, where there are many wren species which are at home in different habitats. In our part of the world too, it seems able to adapt and is found, for example, on entirely treeless islands and bird cliffs out in the Atlantic. The number in Sweden changes a lot between different years, but it is estimated that there are half a million pairs. It is most common in south and central Sweden, but occurs also sparingly far up into the mountain regions.

ROBIN

Erithacus rubecula

THE ROBIN was earlier regarded as a small thrush, but it is more closely related to the flycatchers than to the true thrushes. The long legs and the upright posture betray a life of hopping on the woodland floor looking out for insects, spiders and other small animals. The large round eye sees well in the dark of the forest. Often the Robin gazes down at the ground from a rock or low hanging branch. Its colour pattern should be seen with this in mind. The Robin has a thrush-brown upperside, a particular colour which it shares with the Song Thrush, pure brown in some lights, greenish-brown in others and greyish-buff when exposed to the April light. The rust-red forehead, throat and breast are bordered by a soft grey colour which extends down to the side of the breast. Below, it is light buff or greyish-white. When it moves away from an observer the brown back and the flanks merge into the dead leaves of the woodland floor and only a streak of rusty red is seen and can easily be mistaken for a leaf. At the same time it will, if it so wishes, flaunt its rust-red breast, demonstrating its presence to other Robins within the territory. When it sings at dawn it perches high up in the sunlight. Later in the morning it usually sings from a lower vantage point among the branches. When it hops on the ground, the red breast is accentuated by a whitish patch in the 'heart's' cleft in the middle of the breast.

Robins in gardens

The Robin nests in various types of woodland, often in spruce forest but, in south Sweden, also in parks and gardens with luxuriant undergrowth. It is in the main a migratory bird in the north, disappearing in September and returning in April; however, in recent decades, more and more Robins have begun to winter in Sweden. It has become a regular visitor to birdtables mainly in southern Sweden but also in the central parts

of the country. The great majority of Robins however, still migrate out of the northern parts and down towards southwest Europe and north Africa. During September, most Robins are moving south and then turn up more commonly in gardens. Along coasts and strategic parts of the country they are sometimes numerous and their thin ticking call is often heard at dawn and dusk from thick shrubbery. Most Robins have left Sweden after October, but some stay on if the autumn is a mild one. Towards the end of November the inherent migratory urge has decreased and the die is cast.

The winter singer

The Robin prefers a diet of beetles and other small insects and spiders, but takes advantage also of berries and fruits in autumn and winter. This makes it possible to stay in an area even if the temperature drops below zero. In autumn they establish winter territories, which they defend frenziedly and they mark out their area by singing right through the winter.

If on a November morning, just as it is getting light, you listen attentively, you can get a picture of whether there are Robins in the neighbourhood intending to overwinter. Both sexes sing, but it is mainly males that overwinter. The Robin's song is continuous and chattering, with changes in tempo in which soft rippling chirpy sounds alternate with cascades of lovely ringing notes. This sound, which we in Sweden associate most with spring woods at liverleaf (*Hepatica*) time, is always to be heard in English parks and gardens in winter.

Those which choose to remain in Sweden however, lead an uncertain life and a long hard winter means that many will succumb. Presumably, more and more Robins have found that it is possible to overwinter in towns where they are regularly served with food. By the birdtable the Robin is seen readily picking at small bits of fallen suet or seeds, as well as apples. It probably would not get through the winter if it could not find insects beneath sheltering shrubbery or find bits of suet or other fat. Each feeding site seldom has more than one or, at most, a pair of Robins visiting.

In England, where the Robin is sedentary, it has become the number one Christmas-card bird and is also the country's national bird.

The lovely eye

The Robin always attracts attention by its pleasing appearance, as much for the red breast as for the big attractive eye. Around the rounded and, at the same time, slightly angular black eye there is an orange or yellowish-white eyering which for us bird-painters is always a challenge. The Robin's countenance has an altogether characteristic expression which is created in many respects from the shape of the eye and shape of the pale eyering. The eyering is palest behind the eye and is drawn out into a small lobe. In front of the eye, the colour of the eyering becomes darker and is intertwined with the rose-hip colour on the lore. We often like to read something into the gently gazing eye.

We sometimes hear stories about the bird which pulled a thorn from the crucified Jesus and thereby acquired its red breast. This is an anecdote which is not found written down in any of the texts that make up the bible. The red breast and the gentle eye acquired a different meaning through David Lack. He was a leader in ornithology in a major scientific context and the founder of modern evolutionary biology. His studies of the Robin over many years in the 1930s were gathered together in the first ornithological species monograph, *The Life of the Robin*. Through colour-ringing of individuals, many years' studies and scrupulous notes, we came to understand how the struggle for existence could work for a small bird. English Robins which maintain a territory throughout the year defend it very aggressively. The red breast may be a signal which invites a life-and-death struggle. The big black eye is not always an expression of a gentle disposition.

16 57.

BLACKBIRD

Turdus merula

THE BLACKBIRD is officially Sweden's national bird. In 1915 it was once more voted the winner for this honourable title, after having already held it through an earlier ballot from 1962. It was the Swedish Ornithological Union that organised the ballot and the finalists included Blue Tit, Bullfinch, Magpie and White-tailed Eagle. The Blackbird is common over large areas of Sweden and broadly follows the map of human population density; it is more sparse in occurrence in the most northerly parts of Norrland and in the mountains. It prefers to nest in gardens and many of us see it close by, in city or country, perched quietly in a bush in winter, it can seem almost to be seeking contact. For many, it is doubtless its song on late-winter/early-spring evenings or during fine June nights that leads them to have a strong feeling for the Blackbird.

The old males are coal-black with a yellow-orange bill. The females are brown, often dark brown with a hint of paler markings on the underside. If you see a male that is indeed black but with distinct dark elements on the bill, it is very likely a young male. The bill colour changes however, during the winter months. That of the old males goes from warm yellow in winter to an almost pure orange colour during the peak of the breeding season in May and June. In autumn they can have some dark elements at the base of the bill. On young males the bill is initially all dark, then buffish-yellow patches start to appear and towards the beginning of spring they often have an all-yellow bill.

Thrush moult

The Blackbird male is well suited as an object of study aimed at understanding how passerines moult, in other words how they change their feathers: this can be done well and in comfort from the kitchen window on a winter's day if you put out a few apples. Most feeding sites have one or more Blackbirds as visitors. In the 'Winter birds on our doorstep' survey, 50,000 Blackbirds have been reported and the number per feeding site is three or four. This often presents an opportunity to distinguish the different individuals by close observation of the plumages and bills. Thrushes have, in the same way as all passerines, a first immature plumage, which we ornithologists call 'juvenile'. This plumage is dark brown, spangled with rusty-yellow or rusty-brown spots of slightly varying shape. Such birds are often seen in the middle of summer in gardens. The birdbath and the cherry tree are hot spots for anybody wondering what these may look like. The juvenile plumage of all thrushes and flycatchers is pale-spotted and adapted for avoiding detection in this sensitive period of their life. Young fledglings make up the staple food of the Sparrowhawk's young. The juvenile plumage is replaced before autumn by a plumage more like that of the adults. An immature therefore has two different plumages during its first calendar-year: a first juvenile plumage, which is changed into a first adult dress, the latter then retained during the winter. The time of the plumage change depends on which brood the individual was raised in. In Sweden, some birds are fledged as early as the start of May, whereas others may leave the nest in August. The young Blackbird thereby undergoes what is termed a partial moult, in which the body feathers are replaced while the large wing and tail feathers are retained.

Male plumage

After having undergone this moult, the young males become all black, with a few brown elements. The greater wing-coverts are replaced from the innermost outwards and normally about half of these feathers are exchanged. On the young males therefore, a contrast is created between the black body and dark brown flight-feathers and outer wing-coverts. Most often it is easiest to see the border between black inner greater coverts and brown outer ones. The juvenile retained coverts often have a rusty-yellow tip or outer web which reinforces the colour contrast. The new black ones are, in addition, often slightly longer than the juvenile ones. On old Blackbird males no contrast is seen between the body and the flight-feathers, even though the latter can reflect the light more and look slightly pale, but

young male
adult male

the colour tone is the same, neutral black. Most small passerines breed in this plumage in the subsequent year, while others, such as the crows, do not breed until the year after that, when they are two years old. During its second calendar-year, that is from January in the year after it hatched, the Blackbird male retains this plumage up to the time when it replaces all feathers in the summer and becomes fully adult. A Blackbird in its second winter cannot be distinguished from those which are older.

Female plumage

For the females the principle is the same and the young can also be distinguished from the older ones during the first winter by the fact that their greater coverts present a moult border between juvenile and adult coverts. On females the difference is harder to see since both the new coverts and the juvenile ones are brown. The new ones however, are colder, more olive-brown in tone and lack any trace of a rusty-tinged outer edge or terminal spot. With younger males a certain variation can

young female

be seen; some are black with a shade of red and they also have brown fringes on the breast and belly. They can almost approach an old dark female in appearance, but the difference is usually obvious. As for the females, there is an even more pronounced variation in brownness and markings. For anybody who, like me, loves the Blackbird's brown tones, you can sink into the shades and light effects of female Blackbirds. They are, from a watercolour-painter's viewpoint, more interesting to work with than the black males, however handsome they may be.

Winter apples

In spring and summer the Blackbird lives to a large extent on insects and worms which it takes on grass surfaces or in the litter of the woodland floor. In summer, berry-bearing bushes and fruit trees attract the young birds and a diet of fruit becomes ever more important over the autumn and winter. Most Blackbirds in northern regions migrate southwards during the autumn, mainly in October and November, or move into cities and towns. The many decorative berry bushes that are found in cities generally have a great attractiveness in winter and, on the whole, every hawthorn hedge or barberry shrub has a local or immigrant Blackbird as an overwinterer. In well-established urban territories it often appears to be older males that are wintering; they frequently stay there all through the winter and sing quietly in the bushes.

Almost every year the Blackbird ends up high on the list of 'Winter birds on our doorstep', in around fifth or sixth place. The Swedish population is estimated at some eight million pairs and the Finnish at half a million. Of those which are reported, the overwhelming proportion are found in city regions and in southern Sweden. Garden fruit trees and berry bushes are in all likelihood an important food source for Blackbirds.

On Gotland, every autumn, a large influx of Blackbirds is noted during the period from mid-October to the beginning of November. It is mainly Russian and Finnish Blackbirds on migration. Around my studio and in the nearby area I can at times see about fifty Blackbirds eating pears, apples, rose hips, sloe berries and berries of Swedish whitebeam and hawthorn. As early as January, Blackbirds can start to move back towards their breeding sites, but most birds arrive in March or April.

Way up in the north the passage can continue into May. Those which stay on defend their chosen winter territory vigorously, in contrast to Fieldfares. If, on a cold winter day, you chuck out three or four apples, you will often see one Blackbird, usually an adult, frantically trying to keep rivals away from all the apples. It rarely succeeds in this.

Melancholy song

The Blackbird's most common call is a soft '*kuk*'. If it is more committed it gives a repeated and slightly sharper '*chuk-chuk-chuk*', and when alarmed a hard '*pik-pik-pik*'. These last two sounds can be combined into a rapidly accelerating series, as often happens when the bird is flushed from a bush or flies away. The sound is sudden and clattering, like a window blind being drawn up and can sound heart-rending. If the bird is really worked up over, for example, a cat, it can become a long staccato of dry chucking and shrill yelling '*krip-krip...*' given indiscriminately. Blackbirds also have a very thin indrawn '*tziiih*', somewhat mystical in its pitch, often heard from migrating birds. The song has a nordic melancholy about it, is sombre and clear and seems pensive in its phrasing. Territory-holding birds can 'shadow-sing' (give 'subsong') all year round, quiet chattering series which are usually delivered from within a bush.

adult male with dark on bill

1K hane
26-10.

FIELDFARE

Turdus pilaris

IN SWEDEN, THE FIELDFARE was in the past called the 'snow magpie'. It was known for migrating late and arriving in the south in large flocks along with the first snow. The first thing we hear from such flocks is often clear short scraping '*gih*' or '*glih*' notes followed by a soft chattering '*chaka-chak-chak*'. Often flocks come in large, loose formations, like an armada. In Sven Nilsson's nineteenth-century Scania, these flocks were the last chance of the year to gather in edible birds. Where I live on Gotland, the local birds often begin to move around in groups or small flocks from the end of September, but it is generally not until the end of October or in November that I see any bigger flocks on the move southwards. Rowan, Swedish whitebeam, hawthorn and juniper bushes are thought to be the focus for their autumn foraging in my district, the berries provided in perfect portion-sized packages. In spring it is earthworms that are important: but apples and pears in gardens or in the open countryside are also consumed with great relish. The local birds have usually, with the help of crows, cleared most of the rowanberries when the northern thrush flocks arrive. They stop off however, if there is food, but move on if gets cold and there is a shortage of fruit and berries. It is mostly solitary individual birds that turn up at the feeding stations in winter, even when larger flocks are present in the surrounding countryside.

A forgotten subject

When it was time to paint a Fieldfare for this book, I started as usual to ponder over where in my numerous sketchbooks I have some field sketches. Then it suddenly struck me how rarely I have painted or drawn this species in the field – perhaps I have never done it. Certainly I have

male

painted newly fledged Fieldfare young several times, which I associate with my childhood. When I was small, perhaps ten years old, I always took home young birds barely able to fly in the belief that they had fallen out of the nest. Soon enough I realised that they often hopped out of the nest before they could fly, but my interest in keeping a bird was greater than my intellect. I fed them with worms and thought that they were happy, with their tufts of down on the head, big yellow gape flanges and cocky expressions. They were in some way caricatures of themselves. I had a small menagerie with frogs, caterpillars, slow-worms and every spring a Fieldfare young or Magpie young. But I cannot recollect having tried to create a picture of a full-grown Fieldfare.

Fieldfares nest in my own garden almost every year, so it would have been natural that I had at some time made a drawing of them. All the other thrushes I have painted here in south Gotland, including the rare Ring Ouzel. Perhaps it is a manifestation of the fact that the Fieldfare is altogether too commonplace, but I know that such is not the case. Is it its appearance, its hard-to-interpret face with an unusual marking around the eye and black bags under the eyes and an odd blue-grey colour and the seemingly irregular black spots? Is it quite simply because it is facially a little unattractive that I have never become absorbed in this bird? Despite that, one of the innumerable faces of Fieldfares should have inspired me to get out the watercolour pad, but I do not remember any such occasion. I think that, among birdwatchers, the Fieldfare ends up lowest of the thrushes in status, the species which produces the least feeling of excitement when we focus on it. In autumn we usually look through the flocks to see if any other, rare thrush has sneaked in – at best we find a Redwing, which at least raises the pulse rate a little. Birds which are somewhat uncommon are often accorded an unmerited aesthetical quality in addition; we imagine that we see beauty in what is uncommon.

The ugly handsome one

The Fieldfare is an out-of-tune singer, or in any case a very poor one. If somebody approaches their nests they attack by defecating on the intruder. That wonderful songster the Blackbird is Sweden's national bird while its congener, the Fieldfare, is ignored or regarded as a berry thief. The Fieldfare has never achieved a prominent place in Swedish nature-writing or nature-painting. Gunnar Brusewitz however, painted at least one, but perhaps several, watercolours of Fieldfares. I find it in his first large-format book, *Skissbok* ('Sketchbook') from 1970. It is the only picture I remember. After having hunted out photographs and brought out a traffic-killed bird from the freezer, I set to work. But I am empty, empty of anything to relate. I do not have any of my own inner visions of the type which abound on the internet, if one searches for photographs of the species where it is perched on a snowy or frosty berry-tree branch. I know that I have on some occasion seen a paler female which had an unusually gentle expression, was more timid and had less black beneath the eye, but I do not have a drawing of it. I had to make a late hunt for observations of Fieldfares. The first thing I detected was its call. While other thrushes hardly converse in the autumn, the Fieldfare communicates quite frequently. It reverts to brief attempts at song as if it were seizing the opportunity to rehearse its song;

I think that it sounds pleasant at a time when the Blackbird sounds most like a chicken, '*kuck*' and '*pick*'. And after several different attempts to draw the species I begin to see the bird, recognise its face, understand which parts convey the character. I came to the conclusion that the Fieldfare is, despite everything, both ugly and attractive at the same time. For a comparison one could perhaps wonder if the plumages of the other thrushes were designed in Milan or Paris, with black, buffy grey, brown and a tinge of ochre, whereas the Fieldfare is an odd mixture from London and the 1970s. Yellow shirt with black stripes and squares, wine-red lumber jacket, grey flannel trousers and black shoes.

Distinctive appearance

The Fieldfare is really unusual in its pattern, with an assortment of colours and markings which seem somewhat surprising in comparison with the more sober look of the other thrush species. It has, with varying degrees of saturation, a rusty-yellow breast, heavily streaked, changing into dark spade shapes on the side of the breast and then arrowheads or horseshoes over the flanks. The crown, nape and rump are grey, while the rest of the upperside has a cold reddish-brown tone. The many varying patterns and colour tones make it distinctive and easy to recognise. Males generally have a more intensively streaked throat and bigger black spots on the crown. Females have narrower, pointed spots on the crown which are difficult to see in the field. Young, during their first winter, often retain a few outer greater coverts, which contrast somewhat with the new coverts in colour and pattern. If it is only a pair of the outermost however, the difference is rarely visible. The juvenile coverts are, moreover, usually shorter than the new ones. Old males exhibit a strong contrast between the warm reddish-brown upper back (mantle), which often appears dark-spotted and the pale grey lower back and rump. Young females sometimes have a markedly browner tail and can have a softer and more uniform brown colour on the back and a more buff than grey rump. Some birds in autumn have an almost all-dark bill and this is the rule with young females. Some females have very little streaking on the throat and breast.

I was surprised at how big the individual differences were when I finally began to see them with pencil and brush.

young female
adult male

REDWING

Turdus iliacus

THE REDWING is generally a northern species which breeds commonly in most types of woodland from Småland upwards. It is the most numerous thrush in most of the far northern woodlands and a characteristic species in upland birch forest. It prefers damper woodland with a rich understorey. In Sweden the number of pairs is estimated simply in millions. Some individuals may stay in southern Sweden long into autumn if the supply of rowan berries is good. In cold weather and snow they can then enter gardens if there is fruit to eat.

Smaller than the Fieldfare, being the size of a Song Thrush, the Redwing is easily identified by the contrasting markings on the head and the red flanks. It looks 'tough' with its broad pale eyebrow and submoustachial stripe framing the dark ear-coverts. Most ornithologists have an eye on the Redwing; it gets higher 'attractiveness points' than the Fieldfare. For me it has often been the model subject, because it is more pleasing. The combination of a relatively cool or soft brown colour and the red flanks creates a colouristic harmony. The spots on the underside flow rhythmically like drips from a watercolour brush on a white sheet of paper, on the breast side dissolved as if they had run into a wet surface. It has in addition, in the same way as the Mistle Thrush, paler buffish-grey outer webs on the greater coverts and the flight-feathers, which create a soft pastel-type marking on the wing. Certain individuals, mainly young in autumn, can have a warm yellow-ochre tint on the eyebrow and breast. Young of the year show a contrast between newly moulted inner greater secondary coverts and outer juvenile ones, which usually have a distinct pale, often rusty-tinged terminal spot, these spots forming a little 'string of pearls' along the wing. The juvenile tertials often have a conspicuous 'pinched-out' pale spot at the tip.

BLACKCAP

Sylvia atricapilla

THE BLACKCAP occurs over the whole of Europe and in Sweden is a pronounced migrant. It breeds mainly in deciduous-dominated woodland with a rich understorey of bushes and other plants. Unlike most other warblers, the Blackcap is not a tropical migrant. Most head for southern Europe and North Africa for winter. Warblers in the genus *Sylvia* have a predilection for berries and fruit during summer and autumn, which makes them less dependent on insects during the winter months and the Blackcap is the most common species. Blackcaps in Germany have, during the latter decades of the twentieth century, found new wintering areas in England and a population which migrates westwards has been established. It appears that this characteristic is inherited. When pure residents from the Canary Islands were crossed with individuals from a migratory population in aviaries, the result was either migrants or residents. It therefore takes only one or two generations to develop a new migratory behaviour, which has favoured the Blackcap when the climate has changed.

The species has increased in Sweden in recent years with more and more individuals appearing at feeding stations in the winter. The Blackcap readily eats apple but also takes small pieces of seeds and suet. It is almost in southernmost regions alone that Blackcaps are seen at feeding stations, the species seldom being seen in the rest of the country. For the unaccustomed, the coloration of the male can cause it to be taken for a Marsh Tit. The Blackcap however, is bigger, more elongate and has a characteristic facial expression. The black on the crown is more like a knitted cap, upturned and slightly forward-tilted. It does not extend down over the eyes as it does on the tit and the eye's peering impression is reinforced by a white half-circle under the eye and a mid-grey cheek. Females rarely stay behind in the north; they have a brownish-red skullcap and a slightly warmer tone to the body. Young males too, can have a rusty tinge on the forehead.

male
female
young male with rusty forehead

female
male

GOLDCREST

Regulus regulus

THE GOLDCREST is both an overwinterer and a migrant. Making the right choice is decisive for survival. If the winter is a long and cold one, it can be fatal to choose to stay in the north, while in a mild winter it is favourable to do so. To migrate involves big dangers for a bird that weighs just five grams. Here on Gotland I am fascinated every year by how these small pieces of fluff can set off over the Baltic Sea and succeed in finding their way across a hundred kilometres or more of open water. Many also come in over the sea from the north-east. In some years the flocks of Goldcrests can be like lemming processions in September or early October. The Goldcrest, generally speaking, lives solely on insects and spiders, so the winter presents many challenges. It is Europe's smallest bird and can utilise a niche on the conifers' outermost branches where insects have hibernated. The birds often hover right at the tip of the trees' branches.

The Goldcrest has an expression all of its own. Its charm comes not only from its tiny size but also from the fact that the eye is isolated in a pale area and that the well-marked corners of the bill point downwards. The male has the central feathers of the crown more orange-red, but these are usually hard to see in the field. They are exposed more regularly however, during song and territorial displays. The most common call in winter is a very clear three-syllable '*sih-sih-sih*'.

The species is found throughout Sweden, but is more common in southern and central parts. The population varies greatly between different years but is estimated at three million pairs. Goldcrests join tit flocks which, in winter, roam through the woodland and therefore end up near feeding places where tits visit regularly. They occur only rarely at bird-feeders and then they take bits of suet or fat which have fallen to the ground and small pieces of fat-rich seeds.

LONG-TAILED TIT

Aegithalos caudatus

THE VISION OF A LONG-TAILED TIT usually surprises and fascinates most people. I prefer to avoid using the word 'sweet' to describe a bird, but in the case of the Long-tailed Tit I must capitulate. The head is spherical like a ball, a little ruffled and 'unbrushed' and the black peppercorn eyes and black bill look as if sewn on. The whole body is like a little ball with the odd combination of white, black and dark pink. The disproportionately long tail amplifies the roundedness of the body. At close range one can see a pink 'bracket' framing the eye from above the upper half of the orbital ring. All seem to look alike, but the amount of white on the wing can vary individually. The young undergo a complete moult during the summer and it is not possible to distinguish either the sex or the age of birds when autumn arrives.

Not a tit

The Long-tailed Tit is in fact not a tit, but its size and behaviour can be reminiscent of those of the true tits. The long-tailed tits form a family of their own, with no close relationship to, for example, the Blue Tit or Marsh Tit. The species occurs in a number of geographical races in Europe and the Middle East. Only the northern race *caudatus* has an all-white head, but it is found in a band all the way across to China. In continental Europe, Long-tailed Tits (race *europaeus*) have a dark band along each side of the crown and are a little dirtier in the face. The border separating the different forms cuts through Denmark and various intermediate forms appear, not uncommonly, in Scania.

A Long-tailed Tit seldom appears alone but occurs in small groups of a handful of individuals to perhaps fifteen or more. The flock-members are anxious to keep together and seem to play follow-my-leader through

the vegetation. One flies and so they all fly, in a bounding stream. The gang of long-tailed cotton-wool balls announces its arrival with blunted dry '*pt*' or '*ptrrrll*' notes and trisyllabic clear '*zi-zi-zi*' calls. They are loud, especially when they are in motion and are keen to ensure that all are together in the procession. The groups consist of families which join together, with the addition of the odd bird from outside. The flocks defend a large territory against other flocks, but when the flock splits up just before breeding time the birds do not create any individual territories that are defended. They prefer slightly damper woodland areas, but are found also in cultivated country in groves, bushy areas and woodland strips bordering wetlands.

Traditionally they have not visited birdtables, but in recent years more and more Long-tailed Tits have been observed where there is suet or the like on offer. They also eat peanuts, which have a high protein content compared with seeds of various kinds. Unlike the true tits, which drive away conspecifics, several Long-tailed Tits will gather around a single suetball. Out in the countryside, the diet consists mostly of insects and spiders and only rarely includes seeds or nuts. The dependence on insects and spiders and the fact that Long-tailed Tits do not store food for the winter, make their situation very susceptible to the weather in the north, and mortality is high. During the winter months they roost together and huddle on a sheltered branch in a long row in order to keep one another warm. In addition, the Long-tailed Tit exhibits a form of altruism where males, which have failed in their breeding attempts, start to help another pair with the feeding of its brood. The pairs in the area have earlier accompanied each other in winter flocks and the chances are that they have a certain kinship with one another and that it is relatives that are being helped. The male which helps a neighbouring pair exposes himself to a risk when he utilises his energy to feed another's offspring. The risk is compensated for by the fact that parts of the helper's own genetic material have a greater chance of being passed on through the relative's offspring. In this way this type of altruism, known as 'Hamilton's law', has been able to develop among the Long-tailed Tits. They are very social in their nature.

The Long-tailed Tit is most common in south and central Sweden, but occurs also in south Norrland and along that region's coast. It can be found in the breeding area throughout the year, but the numbers change greatly from one year to another. The number of breeding pairs in Sweden is estimated at 34,000. After a successful overwintering and ensuing breeding season, the population can grow too large and the birds emigrate on a large scale. In some years big movements take place from breeding sites in Russia.

BLUE TIT

Cyanistes caeruleus

THE BLUE TIT is one of the most common and best-known visitors to our birdtables throughout Sweden, including mine. My feeding site at the studio is close to a large clump of trees with well-grown oaks and other deciduous trees, a favourite habitat of the species. In winter bird counts (in January) the Blue Tit always comes in the top five and competes for second place with Tree Sparrow and Greenfinch. The population density is increasing in southern Sweden and the range is expanding northwards. It is however, thinly scattered in Norrland if one tries to find it in the forest interior and it is absent from the mountain tracts. There are about 700,000 pairs in Sweden. The Blue Tit stands out as a true winner in the transformation of the natural landscape that has taken place and is still taking place in modern times.

The ability to adapt rapidly to the environments which man creates is a major reason for its success. As early as the beginning of the 1900s, Blue Tits became known for being ingenious. In England they learned to sip cream from the bottles of milk which the milkman placed on people's doorsteps. Robins also learned the trick and exploited the milk-bar. When, for sanitation reasons, the bottles were then sealed with aluminium foil, the Robins could not keep up with the changes. The Blue Tits, on the other hand, had the sense to peck holes in the foil and were able to continue to partake in the breakfast, served punctually every morning.

The Blue Tit is a generalist and can adapt to different foods, moreover, it has a natural curiosity and instinct for investigation. It scrutinises concealed food resources, which it can open with its short conical bill. The last remaining rolled-up leaves of the oak trees contain overwintering larvae and pupae. The Blue Tit is not timid and is quite tough towards species larger than itself. At the birdtable, suet and fat are favourite food and I often see a dividing-up of the larder such that the Blue Tit works the suetball while the Great Tit eats sunflower seeds. If there is a shortage of one of these or a general overcrowding, they switch food source. The Great Tit is dominant over the Blue Tit, which often gives as good as it gets and sometimes successfully. At suetballs this often ends with the Great Tit working from the top and the Blue Tit from below. Their ways of indicating status to conspecifics are very similar. The Blue Tit often opens its wings and pushes up its shoulders so that the nape is pumped up. It does not stretch the nape however, as it lacks the Great Tit's black tie.

Ultramarine crown

Just as with certain somewhat similar species-pairs, such as Chaffinch–Brambling or Willow Tit–Marsh Tit, the Great Tit and Blue Tit approach each other sufficiently that many authors of bird books feel obliged to describe the differences, despite the fact that the two are in fact very different. The Blue Tit is considerably smaller, weighing about 12 grams, whereas a Great Tit often weighs close on 19 grams. Both however, give a sense of being rather gaudy with yellow, green and blue basal colours. The differences in head pattern immediately become obvious when they are seen side by side. The male Blue Tit's blue colour is really blue and on the crown especially it is brilliant ultramarine. The green colour of the back has a more moderate cold grey-green tone compared with the Great Tit's and it merges into a whitish blue-grey colour across the nape.

The word 'ultramarine' means beyond the sea and refers to the original source of lapis lazuli, the mineral which was ground down to the blue colour pigment. The coveted mineral came from somewhere beyond the Caspian Sea in Central Asia. Exactly as with the Blue Tit, lapis lazuli varies in tints from dark sky-blue to paler turquoise. In 1859, in Finlands foglar ('Finland's birds'), Magnus von Wright wrote of the male: 'The male is an extremely fine bird... forehead white, above it an initially pale but rearwards darker beautiful blue calotte of sky-blue.' Sven Nilsson in *Skandinavisk Fauna* (1858), wrote that the crown is beautiful azure-blue, lustrous. There is something about the colour blue, especially if it is brilliant and glossy as on the Blue Tit, that appeals to us. The male's skull-cap is often obviously bright and it seems that there is a structural quality in the feathers that makes it sparkle. For a Blue Tit the crown

young female
adult male

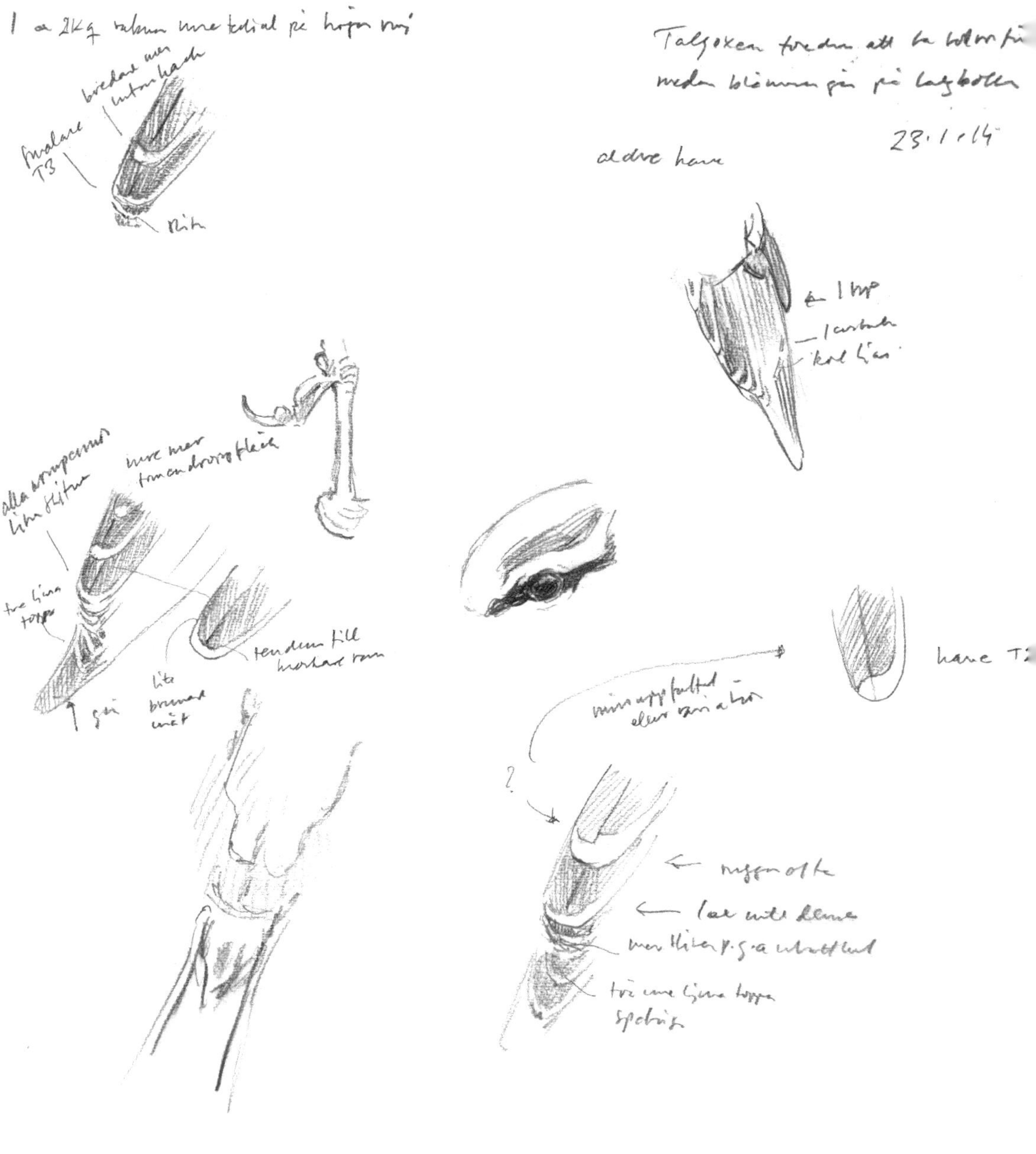

1 a 2K-g vaknar inre tertial på högra vinge

bredare men utan hack

smalare T3

Rita

Talgoxen fredar att ha bollen fri medan blåmesen går på talgbollen

23.1.14

äldre hane

← 1 hp

— 1 armtäck

kal fjäder

alla armpennor lite slitna

inre mer tonande rostfläck

tre fjäder toppar

tendens till mörkare rum

lite brunare mot

går

mina uppfattad – eller variation

hane T2

?

← ruggen ofta

← lar inte denna

mer sliten p.g.a. utsatthet

två inre fjäder toppa spetsig

Äldre hanar
[illegible]
[illegible] ?
mild ton

[illegible] fåglar ~~[illegible]~~
[illegible] inne [illegible] i [illegible]
speciellt [illegible]
[illegible]
[illegible]

I [illegible] på
[illegible]
mot ~~[illegible]~~ [illegible]

[illegible]
[illegible] blå
matt cobolt

[illegible]

nacken [illegible]
[illegible]

Fridarve 17·1·15

shines even more brightly when seen in ultraviolet light. The Blue Tit female chooses males according to their luminosity, an expression of their capacity for survival, their 'fitness factor'. If the female has chosen a male with extra luminosity, she can then let the clutch of eggs develop with a preponderance of males. So, we are not alone in seeing beauty in the mystically brilliant blue crown.

For tits and many other birds, the ability to see ultraviolet light is important, as it means that they can detect the green larvae which seek to camouflage themselves against the young green oak leaves. The males' wings are bright sky-blue, while the females often have a somewhat softer blue tone and some younger females show only a matt greenish tone on the wings. Just as with the Great Tits, there are differences among individuals. The male's wing feathers have a fantastic spectrum of blue tones, from cobalt-blue to pale turquoise with whitish outer fringes and tips on the tertials, like white breakers over a turquoise Mediterranean Sea.

The yellow colour

The yellow colour on the underparts is not wholly identical to the Great Tit's and it varies individually in intensity. When the Blue Tit, on cold winter days fluffs up the belly feathers, the impression of yellow fades even more and it is clearest on the breast. In the middle of the belly, immediately beneath the breast, a dirty-white patch with a darker greyish-black small border or wedge is present, like a memento of the Great Tit's distinct black tie down the breast. Magnus von Wright describes the underpart colour as 'gummiguttgul' (yellow from the rubber tree Garcinia gummigutta), a colour matter now found in the artist's range as gamboge, the latter name alluding to Cambodia, from where, among other places, it was imported. What is very interesting is that a direct association is sought not with, for example, sunflower-yellow or any possible yellow Swedish flower but with some elusive soft yellow colour, which is exactly that of the Blue Tit. I searched among my own oil-paints to try to lay my finger on the tint, or to define it for myself. I stopped at pale Naples yellow, a colour which is distinctly yellow without glistening. It seems to be made to complement the blue of the wing, like dull wrapping paper for a sparkling precious stone.

As with the Great Tit, the young birds replace most of their first plumage during the late summer and acquire an appearance very like that of the older birds. In the wing the flight-feathers and the primary coverts are retained, while the inner three secondaries, the tertials, are changed. A contrast in freshness is therefore seen between these new feathers and the underlying ones. It is often quite easy to determine this if one studies, preferably with the aid of a telescope, the Blue Tits clinging to a suetball.

Silver-clear song

The Blue Tit's calls are quite varied. In the forest a clear '*tzi-tzi-tzi*' is often heard and at automatic seed-dispensers a slightly cantankerous '*churchur-titit*', expectant, or perhaps semi-indignant and in any case, committed. Sometimes the clear sharp notes come first, '*pitzi ti churchur*' and then it seems more relaxed. It is often Blue Tits which remain nearby when one is filling the seed-dispenser and they are the first ones back after one has returned indoors again. The song is a lovely silver-clear series of short ringing notes, '*pitzi sisisisisisisisi*'. Frequently this includes something between song and call, and different variants are often heard, as for example '*pihtzi chu lu lu*'.

Where food selection is concerned, the Blue Tit has many similarities to the Great Tit, but they do differ. The Blue Tit is reluctant to forage on the ground like the Great Tit. What is peculiar to it, is that it inspects various straws and reeds for overwintering lepidopteran larvae. The Blue Tit taps lightly with its bill on the reed stem and can hear if it is occupied or not; if it is, it then pecks a hole in order to get hold of the food. In the branches it is often seen examining buds, galls or calluses which may harbour insect larvae or pupae. Many of the tits are small and when one sees how they climb on and cling to leaves or straws it is easy to imagine that the size is adapted precisely to allow them to inspect the branches from all angles.

The Blue Tit does not cache food, but throughout the winter has to rely on finding sustenance. It is a resident and the pair-members often live together within the territory all year around. As with Great Tits, Blue Tits emigrate on a large scale in some years as a consequence of the broods of young having been large combined with poor seed-setting by plant species which provide an important food base.

GREAT TIT

Parus major

FOR ME AS AN ARTIST THE GREAT TIT is a paradox, colourful and rich in contrasts at the same time as it merges in a fantastic way with its surroundings. When, as often happens, I sketch it and fill in its colours in watercolour, it feels almost exotic with parrot-like coloration. Yellow, green and blue, topped with black and white, it shines out from the paper. When, on another occasion, I look at a bird which is quietly working a sunflower seed in the tree outside the window, the yellow colour can completely sink in among the tints of the deciduous trees' branches. The puffed-up hazel catkins have the same Naples yellow colour as the tit's breast and the grey-blue and green tones constantly brush against all the lichens and mosses of the branches. The black-and-white head becomes a benchmark, or fixed point, which reveals all the time where the bird is among the branches, while the body simply disappears against its background. The yellow colour is always hard to capture, vivid and at the same time sensitive to how the light falls. When as a boy I sat and drew Great Tits, I remember that it was the black head with its white cheeks that I wrestled with and that is still the case. The Great Tit is so well known, so characteristic and yet the bird's entire character and expressions rest on one's getting the right perspective and proportions to the head pattern.

Larger bill in the spring

The Great Tit is a large tit. When clinging to a suetball together with a Blue Tit, it looks thirty percent bigger and with a longer, broader tail. The observer can distinguish the sexes quite simply by looking at the black band down the breast and belly. The male has a broad black breastband which narrows on the centre of the breast and then expands again to form a large black patch on the belly between the legs. The female's breastband

is narrower and more uniform in width and she has only a smudgy grey patch between the legs. Individual variations are great and that points to differences in social status. If you are unsure, you need only look at the belly diagonally from behind: no distinct black patch and the bird is a female.

The bill varies in size and shape. It is relatively long and big: on some individuals it seems to become swollen on the culmen so that it looks heavy. This has, of course, been investigated and it was found that the males in a population in England had a larger bill in spring. This may sound odd, but a bird's bill is not so static as one may think. Basically, it is a skeletal part which is enclosed by a casing of horny material, like a fingernail. The bill of tits is frequently used to work various seeds and nuts and is therefore worn down and renewed.

Social life

The Great Tit's social life and general biology may seem to be an obscure subject for most people, but many years of research have been devoted to just that. Anybody who sits and watches his or her own birdtable will quite soon wonder about the behaviour and interactions of many birds. The Great Tit, which is often the most common at every feeding site, will very soon attract your attention, if it has not already done so. The dominant males help themselves methodically and readily threaten conspecifics by making themselves look big and important. First you see them stretch the head upwards and puff up the breast, demonstrating their size by the black band on the belly. They make the crown flat and broaden the whole nape, creating a contrasty and powerful pattern with the head markings. If

this does not help, they often lower the body and spread the wings so as to appear more impressive. All individuals can in this way score against Blue Tits and other birds. The Tree Sparrows however, generally do not react so much, but remain calm and composed and peck among the seeds. The Blue Tit, on the other hand, understands what is happening and makes a plucky response: if it is not a more dominant male the Blue Tit often holds the fort. There are character differences among individual Great Tits and the characters are to a large extent hereditary. It appears that the more shy males like to keep together in small flocks, where they are not constantly bullied by the dominant males. They are also loyal to these small winter groups of males with lower social rank. The dominant males, those in the habit of taking what they want, will often exchange the group solidarity for the chance to find the optimal surroundings to allow them to feed themselves during the stressful winter. Researchers have also been able to demonstrate that females have a better memory than the males, which may be surprising, do you not think?

When Great Tits from one population have migrated, because of a combination of large broods and poor food supply, the internal competition can become more marked and the birds then develop an ever more aggressive behaviour. This is what happens in some autumns when my island of Gotland and other parts of southeast Sweden are invaded by large numbers of Great Tits originating from farther east. Their appetite for animal fat and protein is not so unusual however, when we think of the species' Swedish name, *talgoxe* (meaning 'suet ox'), or the Norwegian *kjøttmeis* ('flesh titmouse'). The Great Tit eats bits of suet with great relish but also feeds on dead birds and other animals – in their world it is the same thing. It is less common for them actually to kill other, smaller passerines, but this does occur regularly. They may also attack hibernating bats. What is typical is their adaptability and aptitude for scrutinising and making use of unconventional food sources.

A bird at the window

In Sweden, if a bird comes indoors, it is almost always a Great Tit. It is always ready to enter tight spaces in search of food and shelter. Every winter I also see a sooty Great Tit or two which have chosen a chimney

as a night-time shelter. Sometimes I find a dead Great Tit lying on a window-sill in some unoccupied outhouse or an occasionally inhabited cabin. It is often a sad experience but at the same time a beautiful one. Towards the end the tit has puffed itself up such that the back feathers are fluffed up, the nape bowed, the wings drooped and it has become fixed in this posture like a winter standard. Then it is possible really to ponder over the transitions of the various colour tints, the finely chiselled fringes on the wing and the raven-black and white markings on the head.

The Great Tit's palette

The Great Tit's underparts are yellow, as we all know, but which yellow colour? When we look at different individuals we quickly become aware that the yellow colour varies appreciably. Some males seem to be pale cadmium-yellow while others have a weak dirty yellow colour. On males we can often see that the yellow colour of the breast fades on the flanks, only to pass unexpectedly into a pale grey-blue tone towards the rear flank without actually running into green. With young females, on the other hand, the whole plumage is toned down in colour saturation and the yellow becomes varying shades of dirty green when the light is not falling directly on the breast. In our perception however, we see the underparts as yellow and interpret them as such, regardless of what signals the retina's cones give. For a painter aiming to capture subjects in their entireties, this yellow colour becomes an enigma which can be solved only with the palette and paintbrush. And if then... my own failures are numerous.

The males and mainly the older ones, have a distinct grey-blue tone on the wings, giving them a multicoloured impression, whereas females often lack blue tinges and the wing looks grey or greenish-grey and it therefore appears more as if bicoloured, yellow and green, on the body. The mantle varies also, so that the yellowest birds also have a richer yellow-green colour bordering the nape. The wingbar is often yellowish, especially on fresh-plumaged birds in autumn, but towards spring the wingbar usually looks whitish. The females have also a narrower lower border to the white cheek and this can sometimes be almost broken. The males' crown has a Paris-blue lustre which recurs on the throat, but on the breast the band becomes raven-black. The females have less and more neutral gloss on the

[illegible] green gold

winsor green (yellow shade)

permanent sap green

olive green

green gold

[illegible] ([illegible])
Terre verte

neutral grey
(white and
ivory black)

closest to [illegible]

female with grey crown
and drab breast
females

males

crown and rarely any gloss on the throat, which usually appears matt black. The internal pattern of the secondaries and, especially, the inner tertials often creates a nice set of markings when the bird is seen from behind. Where the tertials meet on the folded wings the pale fringes and greyish emarginations create a characteristic pattern, typical of many passerines. The small variations in how the wings overlap or are separated create continual variations in the formation of this pattern. This is all reminiscent of a textile material with a geometric pattern and the way the pattern is continually re-created depending on how it falls over a body in motion. How difficult it is to depict patterns and light effects of this kind without its appearing artificially arranged. Here I often go wrong and the Great Tit is one of most difficult models to 'drape' on the upperside. On one occasion I had a male in front of me which had died by flying against the window pane. This gave me the chance really to explore the pattern of the wing and the different colour variations. In my studies of its tertials however, I was most surprised by the grey colour on the back, something which is in fact never seen in the field. This has a wonderful deep grey tone with both blue and much red in the colour, hard to capture, but far from neutral grey.

Moult

outer tail feathers

Great Tits moult during the summer. The adults replace all the feathers, including the flight-feathers. The young birds change the body and head feathers and also the wing's secondary coverts and tertials, but retain the rest of the juvenile wing and tail. In winter it is often hard to see if a bird is a younger one or not, other than by the fact that the more dull-coloured birds are almost always young females. The colour contrast between juvenile greenish-blue greater primary coverts and newly moulted-in grey-blue greater secondary coverts can be seen on younger males, but is seldom obvious on females. When one holds birds in the hand, that is often an important criterion when attempting to age them in autumn. On Blue Tits one can see a difference between fresh tertials and more abraded secondaries, but on immature Great Tits it is difficult other than on sharp photographs taken at a precise angle. But to look at the various differences and the distinct overall feel, which the colour palette gives between males and females, is often enthralling if you are interested in birds' plumages.

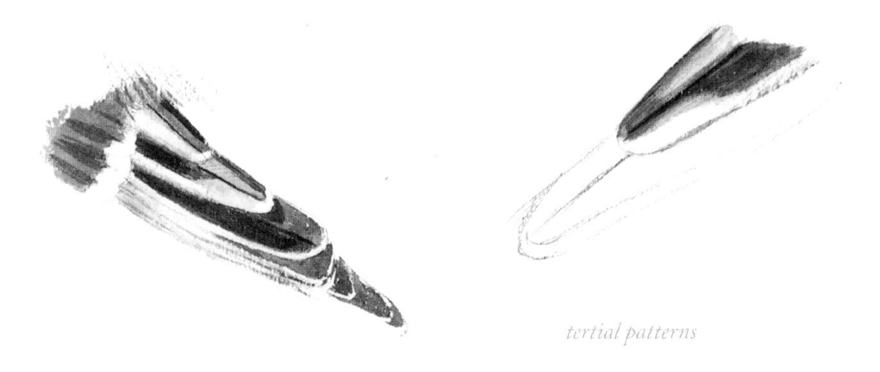

tertial patterns

Role model for population studies

Probably no other tit is so well known as the Great Tit. The combination of being very common, familiar with humans and ingenious in foraging makes it popular, even if the Blue Tit perhaps gets more points for charm. In folk tales the Great Tit had many regional names and was known as the one which came to farmyards to be able to partake of the lard or suet after the autumn slaughtering. Its song was interpreted also as a cry for raw flesh. The whole tradition of feeding the hungry birds in winter can perhaps be attributed to the ingenious Great Tits which searched through larders and storehouses for something small to eat.

Furthermore, the Great Tit is one of the most studied species with regard to population biology: we can confidently state that most of what we know of the numbers, longevity and breeding strategies of small birds started with research studies of Great Tits, first in the Netherlands and later through the comprehensive work which David Lack began at the Edward Grey Institute of Field Ornithology at the University of Oxford. In 1947 Lack started an extensive research project in Wytham Wood, outside Oxford. Like ripples on the water, the study of hole-nesting birds over the years has generated hundreds of doctorate candidates. I think that a dozen PhDs have been determined from the nestboxes in the deciduous woods which surround me in southern Gotland, inhabited by Great Tits, Blue Tits and Collared Flycatchers. Box-nesters are a bigger academic field than most people suspect. An optimal biotope, a mature deciduous wood with much oak, can in good years harbour up to thirty pairs of Great Tits per ten hectares, whereas a little group of Willow Tits with one breeding pair can occupy 25 hectares. The Great Tit is in fact number one on the 'Winter birds on our doorstep' list and there are well over 2.5 million pairs breeding in Sweden. Just as with the Blue Tit, it is caterpillars which have developed among foliage that make up most of the protein diet which feeds a brood of Great Tits. After the breeding season there is a large surplus of young Great Tits which either seek a life in the home wood or choose to move to other districts. Many die however, before they have established a territory and survival in autumn and winter in England and the Netherlands depends on how much beechmast there is. Outside the optimal oak and beech woods it is seeds from other trees and smaller plants that provide sufficient calories during autumn and winter. Great Tits also, like other tits, investigate nooks and crannies in the branches for overwintering insects and spiders. They often forage on the ground, which is more unusual.

Finnish coniferous-forest tits

Despite the fact that the Great Tit is normally a resident, migratory movements are seen every autumn. In some years more extensive emigrations by northern and eastern populations take place. During the early spring of 2015, I had 200 Great Tits at my feeding place during a period when the local birds should have established themselves at their breeding sites. This caused me to study them more closely and I discovered several aberrant, more colourless individuals. The saturation in the yellow both on the underside and on the back and the nape normally differs among individuals. However, these were exceptionally pale and, in addition, had a grey marking on the rear crown which I did not recognise.

A likely explanation offered for the differences in the yellow pigment is that tits, in pure deciduous woodlands, take in more carotenoid through eating yellow-green caterpillars compared with those in coniferous forest. During a few days' sojourn in northeast Finland in April of the same year, in pure conifer-forest habitat, I saw the very same type of 'colourless' Great Tits. It was very likely Great Tits from northeast Finland or Russia that stopped off at my birdtable.

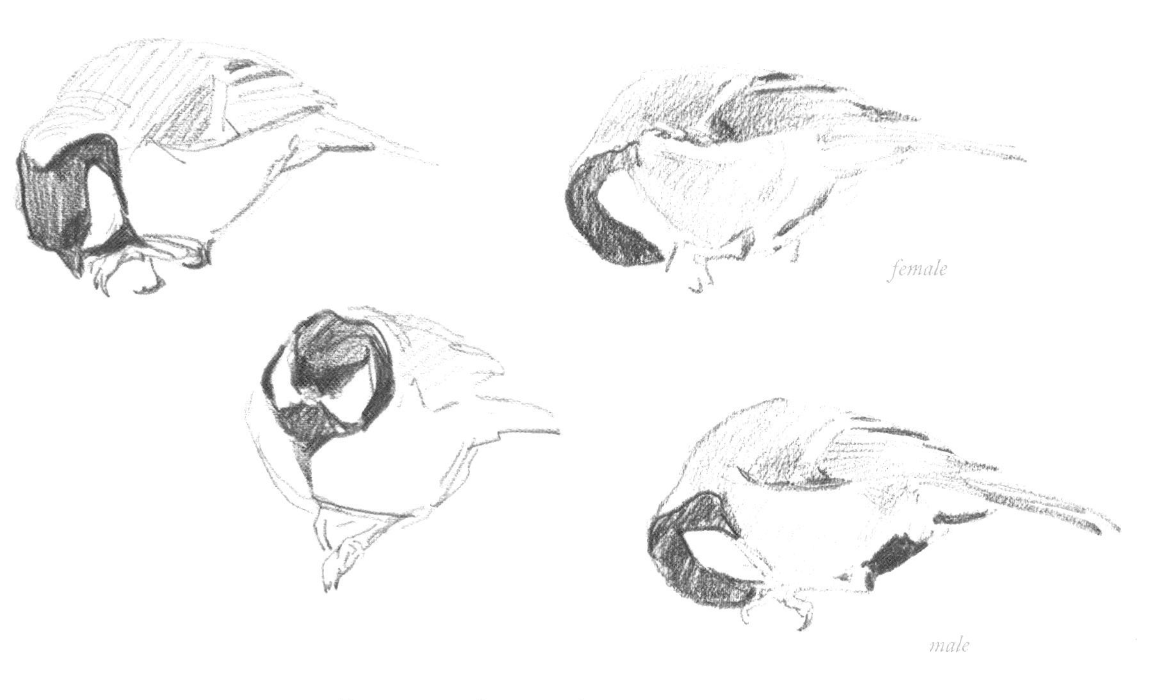

Large vocal repertoire

The Great Tit is notorious for having a large number of confusing vocalisations, both songs and the various calls, in its repertoire. It seems to mimic some other species, and most deceptive are the males, which are the most 'talkative'. Even experienced ornithologists often say that, if you do not know what it is that you are hearing in the wood, it is probably a Great Tit. It is not really so frightful though, as most calls can be recognised by their particular Great Tit-like character. Most often heard is a spirited two- or three-part call with one or two composite notes, for example '*pink-pink*', '*tsui-chi-chi*' or '*huit hiit*', sometimes a more explosive '*pitch-itit*' but also occasional '*tsiit*' calls. The Great Tit sometimes starts to sing as early as the beginning of January and the seesawing song is well known to most people interested in birds. It is usually a two-syllable phrase repeated mechanically four or five times, '*ti-ti-fu*' or '*tit-sui*', in English often transcribed as '*tee-cha*' ('teacher'), but it can sometimes sound quite different. If the bird is agitated or occupied, a grating '*cherr-cherr-cherr*' is heard.

COAL TIT

Periparus ater

THE SMALLEST OF THE TITS, approximately nine centimetres or like a middle finger, is the Coal Tit. Even though it weighs a couple of grams more than the Long-tailed Tit it looks obviously small and tiny and it moves quickly and restlessly like a Goldcrest among the pine needles. It readily comes to the birdtable but is seldom seen in areas with no conifer woods nearby. The head pattern is much like that of the Great Tit and this character means that a field ornithologist will instinctively compare the two species. Many people who are used to having Great Tits at the seed-dispenser often describe the Coal Tit as a very small, colourless Great Tit. The Coal Tit was formerly placed in the same genus as its larger relative *Parus*, but has recently been given a separate genus, *Periparus*. In appearance it looks like a cross between a Great Tit and a Marsh or Willow Tit. If you scrutinise it, you will very soon notice the white vertical band over the nape. The body is in most respects quite colourless, so that the head pattern is what one first notes and then the comparison with a small Great Tit becomes understandable. I must confess that I, as a bird-painter, think that it is difficult to draw the shape, as it is both little and somewhat disproportionate, but it nevertheless has plenty of character.

The crown is raven-black with a fine greenish-blue gloss with white cheeks and white continuing on to the side of the neck. The crown has a small crest which is often raised when the bird is excited over something. The white nape band is not directly visible on the bird when seen in profile. On the Great Tit the white cheek is framed in black, but on the Coal Tit the black chin appears as a large bib drawn out into a triangle at each side. It tends to continue as a pair of dark braces down on to the breast side, hidden under the uppermost feathers. This patterning varies individually and with the angle at which the bird is seen. The back is grey without any green traces. The grey colour can in different lights seem to have a shade of blue or purple in it, but it is first and foremost grey. The

underside is paler but always with a grey-buff tone: in fresh autumn, plumage more saturated and bright. Sometimes the breast side, by the wing bend, can appear a little brighter with a warm ochre colour. The Coal Tit has two white wingbars, the upper one like a tiny string of pearls.

Dependent on conifer forest

The Coal Tit is primarily a bird of coniferous forest but occurs also in mixed woodland. In the literature it is stated that the Coal Tit on Gotland breeds also in deciduous woods and so has taken over the niche of the Willow Tit. However, I have never seen this to be the case. Since it is, in large parts of its range, dependent on the seed-setting of spruce and pine, it can in certain years emigrate in large numbers: it then appears in abundance on headlands and promontories where other migrating passerines gather, but only during autumn in September–October. In Sweden, about 410,000 pairs of Coal Tits breed annually.

This tit is common in many woods on my home island of Gotland except during some autumns when obvious migratory movements are noted, it only very rarely moves out into open country. I have never seen it either at my feeding station beside the studio or at home where I certainly put out food less regularly. Our house is situated about 500 metres from a pine wood where Coal Tits nest every year and the studio is a kilometre farther away. In years with strong migratory movements I have seen them in gardens at home on several different occasions, but the resident pairs are seldom attracted out of the darkness of the conifer forest. Inside the woodland they are almost always heard first, usually in the upper part of the trees and they are often hard to watch for any length of time.

The bill is proportionately slightly more pointed than those of other tits and we may surmise that it is specially adapted for extracting seeds from spruce and pine cones. It also functions admirably as a pair of insect tweezers: the Coal Tit takes on average smaller-sized insects, such as plant lice, compared with other tits. With its small size and pointed bill it is better able to exploit the outer parts of the branches. In the mixed flocks of roving tits it has taken on this job, which it partly shares with the Goldcrest. The birds store food during the summer months and hide it among the broomsticks of conifer needles and in dead male spruce flowers. Stored there are spruce seeds, pine seeds, insect larvae, spiders, small bundles of plant lice and whatever is found to hand during the fertile months.

The Coal Tit has a particular tone in its calls, lisping and not so explosive or cutting as those of other tits. Often heard are plain, slightly drawn-out '*tuh*' or '*tih*' notes during foraging. When the birds are more engaged they utter somewhat faster '*pechi-chu*' or '*ti-chu*'. Many of the calls, as well as the song, have strong similarities in form to the Great Tit's. The voice is however, clearer and sounds a little more cracked and it has a more 'feeble' quality. The song is a fast seesawing series of two- or three-syllable whistles, for example '*piti-chu, piti-chu, piti-chu…*' or '*tit-tsiu, tit-tsiu, tit-tsiu…*'.

CRESTED TIT

Lophophanes cristatus

THE CRESTED TIT is the most pronounced coniferous-forest tit and occurs only where there are mature stands of pine and spruce. It prefers pine woods over spruce. The population becomes sparse farther northwards in inland Norrland and the species is absent in pine forest near the mountains. The distribution is limited to Europe and it extends down across the entire continent and through the Iberian Peninsula. In Sweden it is most common in the eastern parts of Svealand and Götaland. It is not surprisingly absent on Gotland, but also on Öland, which indicates its site fidelity. In Sweden the number of Crested Tits is estimated at 400,000 pairs, on a level with the number of Coal Tits, but the Crested Tit is considerably less common as a birdtable visitor as it avoids leaving its home forest. In one year it achieved last place on the list of the thirty most common species during the January birdtable counts.

In his bird articles of 1921, the nature-oriented journalist Oscar Reinhold Ericson, under the pseudonym Reinhold Winter alias Regulus, wrote that the Crested Tit is contented, cheerful, inoffensive and home-loving. The articles are characterised by an appalling anthropomorphism, but in the case of the Crested Tit it is easy to end up in this situation. When one hears the Crested Tit's genial rolling, almost bracing '*pirillillitt*', the first thing that comes to mind is that the caller is cheerful. I am myself always happy to hear its call, with the expectation of a possible approaching meeting with the bird. At very close range one can also hear sharp '*zit*' calls. It has an appearance that, with its crest and distinct markings, gives it an altogether characteristic expression unlike that of any other tit or passerine. It is also relatively isolated in its genus, which contains only one other species, the Grey Crested Tit *Lophophanes dichrous*, which is found in the Himalayas and central China.

If you do not have a Crested Tit as a visitor at your seed-dispenser and wish to see it at close range, you can imitate a Pygmy Owl if you live in a region where both species are present. It should not be long before first Willow Tits and then Crested Tits come rushing in to investigate the danger while protesting in animated fashion. The Crested Tit then usually raises its crest and stretches its neck. At close distance it can be seen that its iris has a beautiful red-brown colour, unique among the tits. The intricate pattern of black bars and comma-marks on the cheek may appear to be one of the many hard-to-understand patterns which nature has invented, but it presumably has a specific function. It was Dan Zetterström, a bird-painting colleague, who first observed that the Crested Tit has a so-called occipital face. When a Crested Tit is working a seed, clinging to a pine cone or generally not maintaining watchfulness behind it, a nuchal pattern is created which resembles a face. The Pygmy Owl, its principal enemy, similarly has a false face on the nape in order in its turn to avoid predation from raptors and other owls. If the attacking bird of prey believes that its target can see it, perhaps it will abandon its attack.

The song consists often of the call preceded by a clear lisping '*si si*', but sometimes the short rolling series is repeated in a longer shuttling harangue which changes slightly in pitch. The Crested Tit is a true resident and the epithet 'home-loving' may be justified. If you have heard a Crested Tit in a particular woodland area, the chances that you will hear it there again on the next visit are very high. True migratory movements of juveniles, as happens with Willow Tits, are never observed.

As a coniferous-forest tit, the Crested Tit forms an obvious part of the roving tit flocks which we come across in the wood and, together with Coal and Willow Tits, it often constitutes the core contingent. The Crested Tit forages mainly along the middle part of the branches, while the Willow Tit takes the inner sections and the Coal Tit the outer ones. The food in winter consists primarily of stored pine and spruce seeds and of insects and larvae which overwinter in recesses along the branches or which are cached. During the summer months it is mostly insects and spiders. Seeds are often stored in the small hiding-places created by lichens along the branches' middle sections and they may even be covered over with small bits of lichen.

MARSH TIT

Poecile palustris

MY FIRST IDENTIFICATION CONCERNS regarding the twin pair the Marsh Tit and Willow Tit go back to a book by Nils Linnman probably from the early 1960s with photographs of stuffed birds, I believe these were fifty or so of our most common species. On one and the same page in the book there were two mounted tits, the Willow Tit and the Marsh Tit, on which some important details could hardly be made out. The two were both set on a miserable perch against a neutral background and one could easily imagine that they represented a challenge of great proportions for a budding field ornithologist's mind. I begged my father to listen to me and he was amazed that I could separate the two – they looked exactly alike! Linnaeus in his day thought that they belonged to the same species. In Sweden, it was Professor Wilhelm Liljeborg who in 1850, in the transactions of the Royal Academy of Sciences, first described the Willow Tit as a species of its own and separate from the Marsh Tit described by Linnaeus. Whether some important characters emerged from the pictures I do not remember; it could just as readily be their placement on the page that meant that I never get it wrong.

When I then came to explore on my own all groves of trees in Stockholm from Hökarängen in the north to Ågesta in the south, it became apparent that there really was not a big problem. It was something which Erik Rosenberg had written in *Fåglar i Sverige* ('Birds in Sweden'), a book which soon came to replace Linnman's increasingly worn volume. It seemed that their calls usually revealed to which species they belonged long before I could get the binoculars on one of these 'identical twins'. They gradually became relatively commonplace species which were always present there in the woods of my adolescence and no comprehensive studies of plumage characters in the field were ever made, at any rate not that I remember.

When, in connection with this book, I resumed my acquaintance with some species which are absent in the Gotland fauna, the Marsh Tit was found to be less common in my old home district of Södertörn, just south of Stockholm. Its numbers have decreased generally throughout the country and the population is said to have halved in the last thirty years according to recent estimates in the Swedish Ornithological Union's book *Fåglarna i Sverige* ('The Birds in Sweden'). Half of all the country's Marsh Tits are supposedly found, surprisingly, in Småland. The reason for the species' decline can possibly be explained by the fact that our woods contain fewer multi-layered deciduous stands, decaying broadleaf trees and marshy ground; or perhaps it is increased grazing pressure from wild ungulates that has reduced the herb populations at the woodland edge. No fully certain explanation is known. The Marsh Tit often forages among the plant vegetation and the ground layer, behaviour which is more uncommon for the Willow Tit. The populations have however, stabilised in the last decade and the number is estimated at 120,000 pairs.

The most insignificant among the tits

When, in autumn 2013, for the first time in many years, I studied a solitary Marsh Tit at a feeding station at Södertörn, I acted as if I was faced with a rarity. I recorded characters and behaviour in full, tried to take in nuances, capture the expression. It was drizzling and it was difficult to draw. The Marsh Tit was certainly small, like a Blue Tit, but I perceived it in some way as a smaller version of a Great Tit in shape, not so diminutive as a Willow Tit. It perched first at a safe distance and eyed the feeding site. The Tree Sparrows crowded at the edge and it managed to quickly get in a temporary gap and grab some hemp seeds, which it lined up in its bill. When a Tree Sparrow drove it out again, it clung on tight at the edge of the table so as then to take the last seed, as if it had made up its mind to carry a full load back into the thicket. When I came back to Gotland, I was obliged to consult Rosenberg again, just to verify that the Marsh Tit's behaviour appears not to have changed since 1953. He writes that its distinctive characteristic is 'to cram three or four seeds in its bill in one go and that it is very placid. When the birdtable is crowded, it waits and watches on a nearby perch so as, quick as thought, to take the opportunity at the right moment.' It is certainly typical of the Marsh Tit to fill its bill and then move away for a shortish while in order to consume the food or conceal the surplus in a favourite tree. Rosenberg's affectionate relationship with birds finds expression also in the words: 'Even though in appearance the most insignificant of the tits, the Marsh Tit, on closer acquaintance, readily becomes the great favourite.' This sentiment, which never took root in me despite innumerable perusals of Rosenberg's epic work, aroused my curiosity and since then I have not missed an opportunity to look for Marsh Tits in central Sweden's habitats. The majority of people who have a seed-dispenser in the garden, at reasonable distance from the cities, doubtless see this species every day.

As a resident of Gotland however, I am somewhat starved of this 'insignificant' tit. I think though, that it still seems relatively common in suitable biotopes, but it always appears in pairs or one by one. It does not shun the isolated groves, solitary trees or curtains of trees found in farmland. When it searches through a tree or branches its speed seems slightly calmer than the Willow Tit's, less lively and it sets about hiding-places in lichen and crevices methodically and scrupulously and often makes its way down to the ground vegetation. Its bill looks slightly more powerful and the body shape better proportioned. The black crown has a glossiness which the Willow Tit lacks and the nape is less full.

Marsh tit

The Swedish name for this species is entita, meaning 'juniper tit', but it was formerly known as *kärrmes*, 'marsh tit', a name which perhaps better reflects its occurrence if one associates it with a luxuriant marsh bordered by alder and sallow, rather than 'juniper tit' and juniper-bush country. Juniper berries are certainly included in the diet of many tit species, but junipers and marsh hardly go together. The Marsh Tit is still called that (*sumpmejse*) in Denmark, but in Norway it is the 'foliage tit' (*løvmeis*). Its more recent Swedish name seems partly like an adaptation to the Willow Tit's name; 'Marsh Tit' and 'Willow Tit' sound like two species more distantly related to each other. Even more awkward it perhaps becomes if we consider that the Willow Tit on the Continent is more brown on the back and often lives at the edges of marshland and swamps. In recent years these two tits, together with other closely related species such as the Siberian Tit, have been accorded a genus of their own, *Poecile*, having previously been placed in *Parus*. The names 'juniper tit' and 'pine tit' (*talltita*, the Swedish name for Willow Tit) sound good together and give a pointer to their close relationship.

The Swedish word *tita* for these two tits is very likely onomatopoeic and probably refers more to the Willow Tit's song. The Marsh Tit's calls are more like the Great Tit's in pitch, with clearer and less nasal sounds. The song is a rapidly repeated '*chipp-chipp-chipp-chipp*', in tonal quality more like a Greenfinch or House Sparrow. The calls are generally more cutting or sharp in comparison with the Willow Tit's. The Marsh Tit advertises or demands attention with an explosive '*pitsi chip che che che*', the final syllables being very different from the Willow Tit's hoarse '*taah*'.

Marsh Tit
Willow Tit
Willow Tit,
Central Europe
Siberian Tit

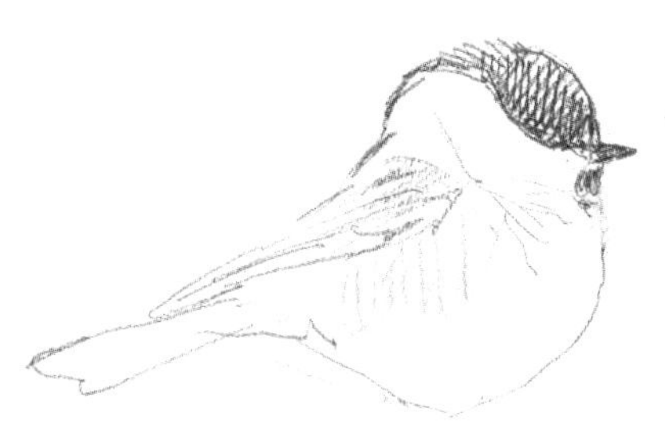

WILLOW TIT

Poecile montanus

THE WILLOW TIT is a sister-species to the Marsh Tit and the two can, to an untrained eye, appear confusingly similar. They are the same in size, mostly grey with a black crown and bib and a contrastingly white cheek. The Willow Tit often has slightly more fluffy or bushy nape 'fur' than the Marsh Tit. It seems to have more head and tail than the latter, in other words the body appears somewhat smaller. When the whole bird is slightly fluffed up, there is very little of the back left before the wings begin.

The main plumage feature is its purer, more neutral colours, lacking the Marsh Tit's warmer dirty brown shades. It is more black, white and grey in pattern and it has a pale greyish-white panel on the secondaries of the wing created by broad pale grey outer webs. The pale wing-panel is usually the easiest character to observe and to use for separating the two species. The underside generally appears greyish-white, but it is not uncommon to see a slightly warm tone on the flanks, as on parts of birch bark, a colour which fades however, in the spring sun and is seldom evident in photographs. Those farthest north tend to become whiter on the flanks and the more southerly ones warmer-toned on the pale areas. The black of the crown is dull, without gloss and extends farther back on the nape. The black throat patch does not always look bigger than the Marsh Tit's, especially from the side, but is less well defined against the breast and tends to expand towards the breast sides. The extent of the patch varies individually and seasonally. A larger panel of black feathers with pale outer webs takes over beneath the black chin and appears more distinct from certain angles. When the plumage is abraded during early summer, the patch often stands out more and becomes more extensive than the corresponding one on the Marsh Tit. The dominant males have on average a bigger patch than females and younger birds. While the Marsh Tit's tail appears firm, straight and square-ended, with

a uniformly brownish-grey colour, the Willow Tit's looks more 'flexible', with a dark centre and silver-grey outer webs. The outer tail feathers are shorter and this can sometimes be observed when the tail is seen from below. The white area behind the ear-coverts, or the extension of the cheek patch onto the neck, is purer white, but it can have a slightly warm tone on occasional individuals. On the Marsh Tit there is usually a distinct difference between the purer white cheek and a slight buff tone on the area behind. The species are approximately the same in total length, but because of the body shape we may see the Willow Tit as being the smaller of the two. Even if they are found in the same woods, it is rare for

spruce seed

them to be seen side by side. The Willow Tit seldom ventures more than a few metres outside the woodland edge, whereas the Marsh Tit readily visits gardens, isolated groves or rows of trees in arable country.

Unlike the Marsh Tit's calls, which are easily mixed together with those of the Blue and Great Tits, the Willow Tit's penetrate through any noise there may be. The winter forest is often remarkably quiet. It is usually the Willow Tit that is first to proclaim that a potential danger is in sight with drawn-out, nasal and loud '*tsi-rsi TAAH-TAAH TAAH*'. Short weak '*ti*' or '*ti ti*' calls may also be heard from a foraging flock. When really excited, it may sound a warning with a sharp '*spit spit*' or a forced '*sisisisi*'. Both sexes sing, the song being a slightly melancholy whistle, slowly repeated three or four times, '*TUH-TUH-TUH*', most similar to the alternative song or call of a Wood Warbler *Phylloscopus sibilatrix*. They also have a quite mechanical rolling '*tze tze tevirr eirr*' which sounds somewhat awkward, as if the phrase was being played backwards. The Willow Tit's Swedish name is *talltita*, the second part (*tita*) being probably onomatopoeic, a reflection of the species' song.

In Sweden a forest bird

In northern Europe we know the Willow Tit as a more pronounced forest bird with a distribution shifted more to the north. The race which breeds here is called, logically, *borealis* and is found all the way up on the mountain slopes where the upland birch forest becomes willow thicket. The distribution follows the entire northern coniferous belt, or taiga, right across Eurasia. The image of the Willow Tit as a northern species is reinforced by the fact that in Sweden the Marsh Tit is restricted to the southern half of the country. The Willow Tit however, occurs in the whole of Sweden but it is generally more common in regions with continuous coniferous forest. In Sweden the population has decreased by 20 to 50 per cent in thirty years. During the last ten years however, numbers have stabilised and even increased in the southernmost parts, perhaps because in many places spruce has replaced deciduous forest. There are about 800,000 pairs in Sweden. The species occurs also farther south in central Europe in a more warm brown form, which is the one first described, race *montanus*, and which is common in mountain tracts, hence its scientific name. The continental Willow Tits are also found in south Denmark, where they look more like a Marsh Tit, but still have the pale wing-panel characteristic of the species. In England and parts of westernmost continental Europe, there is a form which is even more warm-toned, the race *kleinschmidti*. The species known in English as Willow Tit is called 'spruce tit' (*granmeis*) in Norwegian, but the Swedish name *talltita* means 'pine tit', and this can create a certain confusion over which habitat it is actually most at home in. The northern race prefers pine-dominated forest but preferably with an element of deciduous trees, often swamp-forest and marsh edges with decaying alders, willows and birches. The west European populations correspondingly like edge zones beside ponds, streams and old gravel pits where there are often willows and alders growing, but they have no connection with conifer trees. During the winter it is to a great extent the trees' capacity for producing hiding-places for storing seeds and insects and sheltering overwintering insects and spiders that is given priority. Conifers often have more recesses in the bark and lichens, which favour many tits. Seeds from spruce and pine make up an important food source, but various plants, such as large-flowered and common hemp-nettles, also do. During the summer months, the menu consists mostly of insects and spiders.

Winter night

The morning is breaking, it is perhaps 20 degrees below zero and in the middle of February. I am standing in a spruce forest near the mountains in Jämtland, in west-central Sweden, waiting for the first sound from the gloom of the forest. It comes from a few Bullfinches perched in a spruce top, barely discernible. The next sound is somewhat surprisingly from a Siberian Jay, a slightly bubbling whistle. Soon enough I find it at the top of a nearby spruce. I hardly have time to raise my binoculars, however, before it glides past me very close, disappearing again into the gloom of the spruce. This causes a Willow Tit to burst out with a warning, '*ti-ti TAH TAH TAH*', and I am a little fortunate for it was this very experience that I was seeking. Deep within a lichen-invaded dense spruce I see a pale grey ball searching among branches and grey lichens. It is probably an immature bird which has been compelled to get up at dawn to search for food. One more, probably its intended, takes up the theme and the wood seems to have woken up. They have reason to be alert. The Siberian Jay could very well have pinched a Willow Tit for itself in the dim light. The dominant pair in the territory is presumably still fast asleep. The normal body temperature of 42 degrees which made these youngsters jump around quickly and nervously flick their wings has still not been reached in the alpha male and his female. Now at around seven o'clock, before the sun is up, their body temperature is still 36 degrees and it is at least an hour before alert state. They are still resting, perhaps in one of the holes which the Three-toed Woodpecker *Picoides tridactylus* has dug out in the rotten spruce stumps the height of a man. I can hear the woodpeckers' slow but methodical hacking in the background. The younger pair must work hard from early morning until late evening. Their hunting area within the mutual territory is less productive and this must be compensated for by working harder.

My reflections perhaps sound like an anthropomorphising of the Willow Tits, with the alpha pair in deep sleep while the younger pair works its way up in social rank all day long. It is however, difficult to avoid human associations and easy, as fellow living creatures on earth, to be fascinated and perhaps even moved by the Willow Tits' life. The interpretation of the experience and the social order is plausible thanks to many years' study of the life of the Scandinavian Willow Tits. In Norway, Svein Haftorn and Olav Hogstad have for several decades immersed themselves in the life of Willow Tits and other tits and our understanding of these birds' living conditions has acquired a wholly different dimension. Roving tit flocks as a phenomenon and the relative social ranking have been chiselled out in the course of evolutionary pressure from predators and food resources.

Living in a group

The Willow Tit is basically a sedentary bird which maintains a territory in the forest throughout the year. It forms small parties with other tits, Goldcrests and the odd Treecreeper. In these small, loose flocks there is often one breeding pair of Willow Tits and two younger pairs which are not related but which have moved in from nearby territories. The territory is large, often 25 hectares. At a birdtable in winter therefore, we see at most a few stray individuals, since feeding sites are an integral part of a specific territory where no outsiders are allowed to enter. The Willow Tits keep together in pairs throughout their life and in winter it is in a group, together with a further one or two pairs, that they have the best chances of survival. Males are dominant over females and older birds over younger ones. In the centre is a dominant male who defends his female: it is these which nest within the territory. If the dominant male or his female dies, it is rare for a separate individual to be able to fill the gap, but the dominant position in the territory is taken over by the next pair in rank. The solitary surviving bird from the former pair must leave the group and probably very seldom manages to survive to the next season. It is critical to start nesting promptly and get one's offspring on the wing as early as possible. The fledged young which are first out on the course have a greater chance of finding a place in a nearby territory – before it is filled up by the surplus of young tits which are rapidly produced during the summer. Approximately half of the juvenile birds find solidarity in a flock, while others move out of the area. The combination of large broods of young and an imminent food shortage is very likely the reason for the relatively large movements of Willow Tits noted in some years. These movements begin in August and reach a peak in the north during September. When a new individual tries to join a group, it is those which are lowest in rank that have most to lose from a newcomer getting in. They therefore act in a most hostile way towards newly arrived outsiders. A small proportion are left as roaming individuals not belonging to any flock. As solitary birds they have to spend a large part of their time in looking out for predators and have less time for seeking food. The possibilities of their surviving and reproducing are therefore slim.

An internal thermostat

During late summer and autumn when there are plenty of different seeds and insects, Willow Tits conceal these in recesses in the bark and branches of trees. In the mixed tit flocks, the Willow Tits' principal niche is along the inner part of the branches and the trunk. The dominant male, together with his female, then has access during the winter to

the most productive and sheltered parts of these trees. The male makes a point of maintaining his own territory against the younger birds, which have to put up with the lower shelves in the larder, a place which is less rewarding and even more exposed to predators. The difference in conditions for survival is most decisive during the winter, when the days are short and the young birds' vigilance costs them in terms of time. They are under greater stress and devote more time to being watchful for danger, which means less time for foraging. During long, cold winter nights perhaps the fuel is not sufficient. The Willow Tit weighs about ten grams, but when faced with a cold night needs to increase its weight by storing fat reserves corresponding to ten per cent of its own weight. The birds have an internal thermostat which makes it possible for them to lower their body temperature from 42 degrees to 34 degrees during the night in order to reduce the fuel consumption. The dominant birds, which reach the critical weight faster, can end the day earlier, while the younger ones are forced to continue their hunt for food during dusk. The same conditions apply at dawn, when the younger birds begin to search for food at first light, when it is more difficult to detect a predator. In the branches of the trees the dominant pair is to be found higher up and the subdominant lower down, where the risk of a fatal attack by a Sparrowhawk or Pygmy Owl is also greater.

SIBERIAN TIT

Poecile cinctus

THE SIBERIAN TIT is, in many ways similar to the Willow Tit in both appearance and character, as well as in its calls. It has a more northerly distribution, but is found alongside the Willow Tit in the northern part of the taiga right across to Kamchatka. It prefers old pine forest with an element of birch but, like the Willow Tit, it occurs also in pure mountain birch forest in some places. It is marginally larger than the Willow Tit and seems to have even more ample and insulating plumage, which often gives it a markedly bushy appearance in winter. In particular, the head, which merges with the nape, looks disproportionately big. It is generally warmer in colour and the grey-brown ample crown does not contrast with the white cheeks in quite the same way as on the Willow Tit. The crown is of a dull cocoa-coloured tone, with a darker shadow around the eye and the lore. The black bib is big and broad at the base, indistinctly delimited, and it tends to continue on to the breast sides, something which is better developed later in summer when parts of the 'fur coat' are worn off. The breast beneath the bib is dirty white but it becomes more coloured on the belly and on the flanks a beautiful rusty-buff: this colour too, becoming less noticeable during the summer. This tit's colours are reminiscent of those of the Siberian Jay. Perhaps the colour range is adapted to the more lichen-rich northern pine forests where pine bark, pine scales, beard-lichens and urn lichens provide excellent hiding-places in which to store pine seeds, juniper berries and caterpillars for dark winter days.

The Siberian Tit joins other tits during the non-breeding season but normally keeps within its territory. It is basically sedentary but, as with the Willow Tit, in some years juveniles undertake movements far outside the home areas, then often in the company of Willow Tits. They can then turn up at birdtables in central Sweden, so there is reason for birdwatchers there to keep a look-out for this Lapland tit. The population is considered to be stable.

Its calls in many ways recall those of the Willow Tit, especially its '*pitsi CHAY CHAY CHAY*', but it possibly has some of its own which distinguish it, including a rolling or chugging '*ch churrl*'. The song also contains notes with vowels which are more rolling. Instead of the Willow Tit's melancholy '*tuh-tuh-tuh*', the Siberian Tit may repeat a more bleating '*tschruuh*', in tone reminiscent of the Brambling's song.

TREECREEPER

Certhia familiaris

THE TREECREEPER is doubtless mainly an adjunct to the tits at your seed-dispenser. It is a member of the roving tit flocks which move through the woods and therefore naturally turn up close to birdtables. However, it often does its own 'thing' nearby on a tree trunk, woodpile or stone wall. It seeks out insects and spiders in bark crevices and lichens. It does sometimes visit suet put up for birds. This behaviour was already described by Magnus von Wright in 1859: 'He inspects tree trunks (often on spiral path) from base to top, from where he flies down to the base of another tree, for he cannot, like the Nuthatch, move head first downwards.' It usually dives down to the next tree when it has worked its way half up the tree, or sooner. It also inspects thicker branches. The long, needle-thin bill means that it can exploit a niche which others cannot reach. The eyes look a little slanting and are positioned such that the bird will be able to look in among the smallest nooks and crannies; perhaps it can be described as extremely near-sighted.

When the bird creeps up a trunk it generally appears pale and plain, with a long, pointed brownish-buff tail and a chalk-white belly. The entire upperside is spangled with slightly untidily arranged whitish drop-shaped spots on a brown or chestnut-coloured background. It is most easily detected by its piercing calls, a very thin and high-pitched '*si*' or '*srrri*'. The song is a meandering clear series ending with a slight flourish, '*sitt-sitt-sitt sitte sitte-sitterroitt*'. If you have learnt to recognise its call, you discover that it is very common in most woodlands. The population in Sweden is estimated at 750,000 pairs. The Treecreeper is a resident, but every year some migration from more northerly regions occurs and in some years significant migratory movements are noted.

male europaea
male asiatica

NUTHATCH

Sitta europaea

AN ODD BIRD which attracts attention when it comes to seed-dispensers, unabashed to the point of being boorish, mobile in all directions, always on the go. It has a lovely grey-blue colour over the back and crown, a whitish breast and a black band through the eye continuing down over the neck, which gives it much character. It looks tough. In winter it feeds on seeds and nuts, mainly hazelnuts and acorns. At a feeding site, it is often a sedentary pair that comes with great regularity and collects a bushelful of sunflower seeds or nuts. Despite its specific adaptation for climbing on trees in all directions, it skips around with ease on the ground, searching for fallen nuts or seeds. These it carries away in its bill for a shortish distance and caches in the bark of an oak tree. Stands of larger oaks with their coarse bark are what the Nuthatch prefers most, but all trees with fissures and hollows are perfectly suitable. If it wishes to open a hazelnut, it wedges the nut firmly and works it with the bill. Nuthatches can be found also in mixed woodland and more rarely in conifer-dominated woods; eastwards in Siberia it is larch trees and Siberian pines that provide the staple food. When the adults are feeding their young, it is usually insects and spiders that are the prey.

The Nuthatch is common in south and central Sweden, but it also occurs sparingly, in southern Norrland in mainly coastal regions. Observations farther north, in Västerbotten and Norrbotten, are mostly of the Siberian race *asiatica*, which turns up periodically after invasions from the east. Nuthatch numbers have grown in the last thirty years. The reason for this is not clear, but it is perhaps connected with the fact that we now have milder winters compared with the cold decades during the middle of the last century. In Sweden there are almost 200,000 pairs.

Loud

In almost all woods, if there are some deciduous trees, Nuthatches can be heard. They are loud, both in spring and in autumn, which is why they are immediately noticed. If you are well acquainted with their tonal quality, they are easy to recognise; the sound has a nasal or hollow ring and a bouncing character. Most often heard is a series of somewhat irregularly repeated '*dyeet*' or '*dyut-dyut*'. If they are excited and warning of danger, the tone is sharper and can become almost vowel-less, fast '*tvett*' series that can almost become a staccato. In spring both sexes sing with more melodic slower notes, '*piiuh piiuh piiuh*', or faster series of '*pi-pi-pi-pi...*'.

Differences between female and male

The sexes can usually be easily separated by the colour of the vent and rear underbody. The undertail-coverts have a slightly peculiar character. They consist of two parts, a downy slightly fluffy base and a solid cup-shaped snow-white tip. The male has a horse-chestnut-red colour at the base giving a greater contrast, while the female's is a paler and dirtier rusty brown. On males the chestnut-red extends over the rear flanks and contrasts with the otherwise white underside, while the rusty tone on the female does not spread over a larger part of the rear body and does not contrast. On some males a large extension of the brown-red colour along the flanks is apparent, while on others the colour is more restricted. With its distinctive and unique colour pattern the Nuthatch has always been easy to recognise and has hardly attracted any in-depth studies from field ornithologists.

Gotland's Nuthatches

In recent years when following the life in the clump of oaks outside my studio, I have pondered over differences in the underside colour of Nuthatches. Sometimes I think that they are unusually rusty-coloured below, in a way that I do not recognise from my childhood days near

Stockholm or pictures from other parts of Sweden. Not uncommonly I see individuals, females, which have a distinct rusty tone all the way forward to the sides of the neck and I have then wondered if we have got odd continental or British Nuthatches, of the race *caesia*. The Nuthatch is however, highly sedentary in Sweden and should be so also in the rest of Europe. How have they at some time come to Gotland, when Marsh, Willow and Crested Tits have never made the journey? Nuthatches of the nominate race, *europaea*, from regions east of Gotland, in European Russia, are generally the most white-bellied. Clearly, they may in some years move westwards and be seen in south Finland, where the Nuthatch is otherwise absent. These however, cannot explain why Gotland's Nuthatches have developed a more coloured underside. Perhaps they originate from the first wave of Nuthatches which accompanied the oak tree northwards after the inland ice had released its grip on Scandinavia.

female with buffish-coloured underside

Or else I have quite simply not looked closely enough at what the Nuthatches look like in Scania or Västergötland.

Siberian and continental Nuthatches

When new generations of books on Europe's birdlife were published in the 1960s, one could, as a young field ornithologist, quickly learn that there was another race of Nuthatch elsewhere on the continent, *caesia*, with rusty-buff underparts. The Nuthatch is familiar with humans and easy to photograph. Pictures of English Nuthatches with rich rusty-orange underparts perhaps aroused a certain wonder, but I think that few of us active ornithologists deliberately sought to see Nuthatches outside Sweden just to see this variant. There are other examples, such as the Willow Tit, where Scandinavia and northeast Europe have whiter-bellied populations.

A very different interest among Swedish ornithologists however, was accorded to the central Siberian race *asiatica* when it turned up in Norrbotten in the mid-1970s. Anything coming from Siberia has always had a special attraction for us who, in autumn, are vainly longing to discover a Siberian passerine. The Siberian Nuthatch too, is a further race, but it initially attracted great interest which resulted in a series of articles on its appearance and behaviour. I believe that I first became aware of this little visitor from regions east of the Urals in an issue of Vår Fågelvärld after the 1976 invasion, when two breeding attempts were confirmed in the following spring. For my field guide which I wrote at the end of the 1980s, I went very carefully through how this form looked, but then there was never any attempt to see it in real life and I still have not seen it. So, now I again have reason to paint this form, it is once more from published descriptions. Then there were only a few published photographs, but now one can download loads of photos by 'googling' the race.

The Siberian form is smaller and has a distinctly more slender bill with a finer point, paler blue-grey back and whiter underside. It also has more white in the supercilium and in the forehead, but the local form too, not uncommonly has a little white in the supercilium, though rarely or never distinct white on the forehead. For ornithologists in Finland and north Sweden the race *asiatica* is now well known. Real sharpness in the descriptions comes only when a wholly normal Nuthatch accidentally turns up

at a birdtable north of Sundsvall. Therefore I quote Rolf Gustavsson, who in *Fåglar i Norrbotten* ('Birds in Norrbotten'), in 2001, wrote about the first discovery of the nominate race *europaea* in Norrbotten: 'The bird's size, its bill size and shape, its back colour and its underpart colour are in that order what makes me react to whether the Nuthatch may be *europaea* or *asiatica*.' From photographs it strikes me that the Siberian in addition appears to have a different tarsus colour, the nominate race having a clear buffish colour whereas asiatica is grey or greyish-black.

JAY

Garrulus glandarius

THE JAY is Sweden's most common corvid, which may surprise some when we see large flocks of Jackdaws in the lowland areas or Hooded Crows almost everywhere. Not until September, when the Jays begin to fly between the coniferous forests and oak hills in the more open countryside, do we become aware of their numbers. They then gather acorns and hazelnuts in readiness for the winter, hiding these within the territory. This is a bird which for the greater part of the year lives relatively anonymously in both mixed and coniferous woods. Its numbers have decreased somewhat in the last thirty years according to *Fåglarna i Sverige*, and the population is estimated at about 300,000 pairs. It is more numerous in the southern part of Sweden and breeds also, sparsely, in the interior of Norrland, but is absent in the mountains. In winter Jays remain in the country, but in some years larger migratory movements are seen during the autumn, these very likely due to a combination of a good breeding season and a scarcity of acorns and nuts. The majority of these birds which move southwards in small, loose flocks are juveniles.

This is a frequent visitor at feeding stations, where it readily fills its bill and crop with sunflower seeds, hazelnuts or peanuts, whatever is on offer at the time. It usually flies off to cache the food and then returns after a while to continue. At my place, there are often two or three Jays which take turns to visit. They also like suet and fat and they are most frequent as visitors in winters with plenty of snow. The Jay usually arrives on the scene by gliding in and it immediately stands out as being highly variegated and big and ungainly compared with the smaller passerines. It is rare that one has the opportunity to observe Jays in the forest, where they are often a little cautious and tend to be shy.

A beautiful plumage

If one or more Jays have learnt to visit a place where food is provided, one has the prospect of observing this wonderfully attractive bird. The combination of soft greyish-pink, brownish-pink and greyish-mauve colours and sharp white, black and horse-chestnut brown would cause any fashion stylist to be taken aback. The creation is topped with the shimmering blue brooch on the wing. This model however, is perhaps not the most fair that evolution has created, from a human point of view. It looks altogether a little malicious with its whitish-grey eye, rings around the eyes and jet-black drooping moustache. When perched on a branch and watching, with slight head movements, it presents plenty of character, perhaps it could be expressed as charm and I cannot help seizing my lead-pencil. The Jay is a 'Karlsson on the Roof' figure. The crown is bushy and can be raised like a pixie cap when the bird has reason to be agitated or excited. It is most uneasy at the sight of a Goshawk, which immediately causes loud screaming '*gaaah*' calls, and great alarm. Sparrowhawks and other raptors attract displeasure, but they are rarely regarded as a major danger. Sparrowhawks however, are often visibly irritated by the fact that their own arrival is clearly announced by the Jays and I often see the Sparrowhawk chasing after Jays but more in order to drive them away from its own hunting grounds.

The Jay can hardly be confused with any other bird but, as Erik Rosenberg wrote in *Fåglar i Sverige* ('Birds in Sweden'), it is often the object of questions and wonder from people who do not have a direct interest in birds. If it turns up outside the window or flies across the track in the forest it presents an almost exotic impression. The blue patch on the wing opens up and becomes bigger and even more flashing in flight, as do the white and black areas on the wing and tail. Nothing of this is particularly prominent when it is flying at a slightly higher level, the movement then being flappy, the tail long and the wings broad and rounded.

acorns

Evolution's brush

As an artist one can be fascinated by the visible effect the wing patterning is trying to achieve. As humans we may be fascinated, but we realise at the same time that what we ourselves see as peculiar and perhaps beautiful must produce reactions of a similar, but nevertheless entirely different kind, in others of the bird's own species. The black secondary coverts next to the blue-vermiculated outer coverts are slightly elongate and rounded and fall exactly into the white patch. The design is no chance event but created from its visual effect, a brushstroke from evolution. The blue marking is on the alula, the greater primary coverts and the outer greater secondaries; the ground colour is a pale whitish-turquoise and this is then vermiculated with dark navy blue edged with a cobalt-blue shade. On young birds the bar code is slightly more irregular and with fewer bars. In the field however, there is hardly ever time to try to count or estimate the nature of the markings. I can only wonder at it.

Screams, mews, babbles

The most common call is a drawn-out loud, screaming and hoarse '*aaaak*'. Less common is a Buzzard-like mewing, which is often bewildering in the forest as the bird is rarely, if ever, seen when this call is uttered. The Jay sings with chattering and babbling sounds at varying high pitches and clattering sounds.

SIBERIAN JAY

Perisoreus infaustus

THE SIBERIAN JAY is like a painting of its surroundings with greying older spruce bark, rusty flakes from pine branches, and a soft 'hairy' feather clothing as if of beard-lichens and horsehair-lichens. It can hardly be confused with any other bird species. The female and the male are alike in appearance. It looks light in weight and glides silently for long distances without any wing movements, clings to trunks and hangs upside-down when inspecting dangling lichens and recesses for food. The Siberian Jay is a special bird which has adapted to a winter climate in which the temperature often drops lower than 40 degrees below zero. It stores food in autumn, primarily pieces of fungus and berries, but also snails, insects and spiders, which it carefully hides away and covers over. These are cached in crevices in rough bark and at first also on the ground. Before the snow falls the store is moved up to above the predicted snow-cover level. Its relatively short bill is no good for digging in snow, unlike that of the Nutcracker. The Siberian Jay belongs to the taiga, the northern coniferous belt and occurs in Sweden south to the Dal River (Dalälven). In Norway it reaches slightly farther south, down to Telemark. It is most common in lichen-rich older coniferous forest in interior Norrland and in conifer forest near mountains.

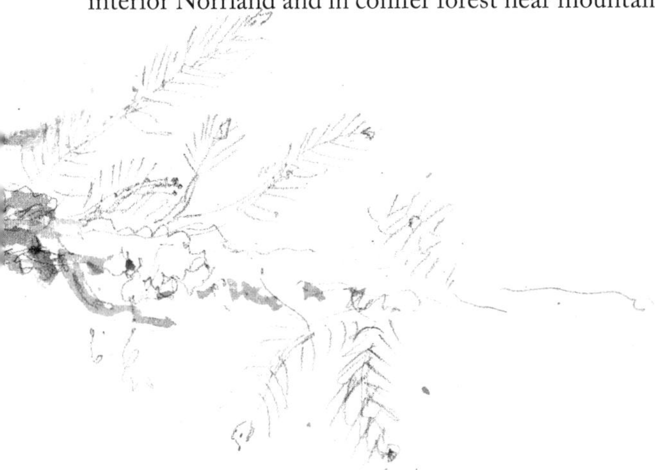

The bird of ill omen

The Latin species epithet *infaustus*, which means 'unlucky', is perhaps explained by this bird's unabashed way of approaching man's food supplies when these are running short. Linnaeus mentions the Siberian Jay in his Lapland travels *Iter Lapponicum* (1732): 'The Lapland magpie, the red bird in Västerbotten... is mean, steals meat and anything she sees, is not timid.' Sven Nilsson, in *Skandinavisk fauna* (1858), adds that it consumes birds that have been caught in snares, 'e.g. grouse of all kinds, so that only the carcase remains'. Erik Rosenberg writes in *Fåglar i Sverige* ('Birds in Sweden') in 1953 that in winter 'it turns up at lumberjacks' camps to get hold of meat or fat', a not entirely flattering character description. Perhaps the picture has gradually changed over time. The birds' fearlessness and precocious attitude towards an occasional food source have perhaps not always been fully appreciated. Nowadays most people who go skiing or walking in the northern forests probably regard the Siberian Jay as a curious but attractive and welcome guest when the sandwiches are brought out of the rucksack. Maybe the settlers in Norrbotten in those days considered that the Siberian Jay's sudden and unannounced appearance boded misfortune. The bird does have something mystical about it, in the same way as the Nutcracker in the south does.

The spruce dance

All who have met Siberian Jays in the forest seem to have similar experiences. First a call is heard, then the bird is seen in the top of a spruce, only in the next second to glide silently in and settle very close by, watching, wondering. Then one more comes and one more, perhaps another one. If nothing is offered or is of interest to them they soon disappear back into the spruce forest, swallowed up by it. The person who more than anybody else came to know the species was Arne Blomgren from Norrbotten. His studies of the species were published in 1964 in the book *Lavskrikan* ('The Siberian Jay'). He became very familiar with his Siberian Jays, which he followed for many years, one female for all of twelve years. He could carefully stick a finger beneath the incubating female and then lift her up to see how many eggs she had laid. He describes the species' amusing displays with tossing and bowing of the head, jerky movements and tremendous aerial exercises. Some of this display is what Blomgren calls the spruce dance and he gives an example: 'The male sat in the top of a spruce. Suddenly he dropped straight down, with wings close to the body. Reaching the lower part of the spruce, he spread his wings and swung into the branches of the spruce. There, as if possessed by an evil spirit, he whirled around the trunk and up and down among the branches, the wings clattering.' It makes me wonder where our own traditional July dance around the spruce comes from.

In Norway, Gunnar Borgos and Olav Hogstad have pointed out that fungus makes up an important part of the food which is stored for the winter. The fungi which the birds store are often common edible mushrooms, but they regularly take fly agaric too. The latter, when consumed, produces a mild atropine-like effect such as hallucinations, elation and frenzy, as with the beserker Vikings in a trance-like fury. The question is whether the spruce dance developed during a state of intoxication of this kind.

Family groups

The Siberian Jay lives throughout the year and throughout its life in small groups of five or six individuals within the territory. A breeding alpha pair is accompanied by a pair of birds from its own earlier brood and one which has come from another territory. The immature birds do not help their parents with the rearing of the young, something which does occur among some other members of the crow family. The adults however, are more benevolently disposed towards their own offspring than towards the birds which have come from outside. A small group means more eyes and ears against predators and for discovering chance food sources. They nest early and are therefore dependent on their cached supplies. They often visit birdtables, where they prefer suet or fat over seeds.

This species has a number of different calls depending on its state of mind. The most common call is a soft mewing Buzzard-like '*myayk*', which announces its arrival and sometimes it gives a more distinct '*kvook*'. If it is agitated, slightly hoarse and shrill '*errk*' calls are heard, if excited often in series, '*ayrk ayrk ayrk*'. The quiet song consists of a chattering twitter and weakly squeezed-out sounds.

MAGPIE

Pica pica

THE MAGPIE is one of our best-known and also most popular bird species. Our relationship with the Magpie, however, is equivocal. We like it for its appearance and its occurrence near our habitations, but dislike it for its aggressive nature and its reputation for thievishness as well as the fact that it takes eggs and young from other birds' nests. However, the Magpie's interest in shiny objects is a myth. In former days Magpies could be kept in captivity and they are always interested in inspecting various objects and are not slow in helping themselves to food left unattended. It is the melodrama *The Thieving Magpie* (*La Pie Voleuse*) from 1815 and Rossini's 1817 opera *The Magpie* (*La gazza ladra*) on the same theme that have given the Magpie this undeserved reputation. Scientific experiments have shown that the Magpie has no preference at all for shiny objects. But cause trouble they can; I do not know how many times I have sworn over the Magpies which have made holes in the compost bag which I put out on the doorstep the night before. They are in addition quite distrustful and quick to fly away when approached, as if they had a somewhat guilty conscience.

The success of the Magpie and other corvids is all about their ability to adapt to a changing world and to function in urban environments. Its interest in examining everything new, in testing it and a capacity for abstract thinking, make the Magpie a winner.

A Magpie pair indicates life

The Magpie, Hooded Crow and Jackdaw have approximately the same populations in Sweden and are all, in various ways, tied to human habitations and agricultural landscapes. The Magpie is in many respects a town bird, a species which seems to thrive best in suburbs and residential districts. Nesting Magpies denote life: only if the farm is inhabited is there a pair of Magpies keeping check on the site. In our neighbourhood there is always a Magpie pair around every farmyard or groups of yards. They perch in a tree or on the cowshed roof in the morning and from there they make flights out among fields and pastures; there is always a Magpie in the landscape, decorating a hawthorn bush or hopping around the lambs in the wooded pasture. Some distance away the Magpie announces its presence: I am the one perched here and I live here. Their appearance is like a logo, a recognition factor. The number in Sweden is estimated at 220,000 pairs and it is a pronounced resident.

Design in black and white

Were it not for the fact that it is so common, this species would perhaps be placed among some of our most attractive birds. The entire head, the breast and the back are quite dull black, a little velvety black. Against this the white shoulders look like a newly ironed white silk shirt. The belly is more like a knitted white angora sweater, soft and bushy. The lower belly can be in shadow, whereas the shoulders seem always to be whiter than snow or than the clouds in the sky. It is clear that Magpies work with contrasts as an attraction, sooty black against white, together with the shimmering rainbow effect of the wing and tail feathers. The gloss or shimmer from the black plumes of many corvids is a structural effect within the barbs of the feather's vane. The colour reflected depends on the angle at which the light is falling. The secondaries of Magpies can therefore appear green in some lights and blue in another. The tail is longer on males than on females and longer on older dominant males than on younger ones. The central, longest pair of tail feathers, when fully developed, is convex in shape, which makes the tail look somewhat club-shaped towards the tip. At a certain angle the tail looks entirely black, but with the light falling at a ninety-degree angle the tail is dark metallic green. Near the tip it becomes rainbow-coloured, from yellowish-green through purple to violet and, on the outermost part, blue. The black colour in a feather makes it more durable against fading and abrasion. On the folded wing, normally little or no white is visible when the bird is perched. When the Magpie then takes wing, the hand bursts into white, a magical quick-change turn. The

individual primary feathers are predominantly white, being black only on the surfaces that are exposed to the light when the wing is folded. In the Magpie's world it seems as if contrasts are 'sexy'. Sometimes a thin band or lines of white show through on the perched bird and when the wing is hanging a little loosely and relaxed the white is clearly visible.

Life in the suburbs

In semi-urban environments the Magpie pairs have taken over all gardens, parks and greenspaces and they defend these against neighbours. One can easily draw parallels with the patterns of life in residential and terrace-house areas. Every Magpie pair keeps a careful eye on what its neighbours are doing and just before the breeding season they are especially watchful. The risk that the male neighbour will sneak in over the hedge and 'flirt' with the female and copulate with her if she is left unguarded, is great and therefore the pair-members are almost always seen together during the most sensitive period. Infiltrators are properly scolded by the pair, but only if the male or female mate is present, otherwise a 'friendly association' is often initiated if the visit involved the opposite sex.

The groups of Magpies which are often seen on winter evenings, where several gather in a tree or shrubbery, consist of young birds which do not have a territory of their own. During the day they travel around and make life unpleasant for the established pairs. When such a gang of youths settles in another one's area, the territory-claiming male must remonstrate with it. If he is a bit weak, he can lose a part of his territory to some cocky youngster. The Magpies' social display, which goes on all the time in the district, is often more complex than what we see in occasional observations.

Humming to itself

The sound which we most often hear from the Magpie is a slightly hoarse '*cha*' or '*tschak*', often in a laughing series, '*cha-ya-ya-ya*', while the tail and the wings are drooped. On a sunny day when peace and quiet prevail Magpies can sometimes be heard singing quietly inside a shrubbery, softly chattering, squeaking, grating notes which are hardly territory-marking sounds. A Magpie behaving thus seems mostly to be in good spirits, quietly humming to itself.

Food

Like most members of the crow family, Magpies are generalists which can accept most of the seeds, fruits, insects, small animals, eggs, bird young and carrion available. They are however, capable of killing rodents and fairly big young birds. At feeding stations they help themselves to most items. Seeds and grain they pick up and cram into their crop, later placing them in a more undisturbed site. Pronounced collectors of food like the Nutcracker or Jay they are not. They readily gather up food if there is an abundance of it, but most is usually used up before long.

NUTCRACKER

Nucifraga caryocatactes

THE PEARL-BESTREWN CROW of the deep spruce forest and moss, mystical and retiring. P. O. Swanberg devoted a great part of his life to studying the Nutcracker's ways of life and he came to be a kind of idol for me in my early teens. When I was fifteen I wanted to become a dentist and an ornithologist, just like P. O. His courageous fight to save Hornborgasjön from drainage companies and authorities I had poor knowledge of at the time. It was his ability to get close to the life of the Nutcracker that impressed me, this ability to become close 'friends' with a bird as shy as it is attractive. Most of what we know of the Nutcracker's biology came from his detailed and patient studies on Billingen, in Västergötland. Those which breed in south and central Sweden are totally dependent on hazelnuts but nest in dense spruce forest or spruce-dominated forest with moss in the ground layer. The distribution is therefore patchy. Nutcrackers also breed in spruce forest in mountain regions in central and eastern Europe and here the principal food is both hazelnuts and the seeds of cembra pine. The population in Norrland belongs to a different race, the so-called Slender-billed Nutcracker race *macrorhynchos*, which originates from Siberia and feeds mainly on seeds of the Siberian cembra pine. The Swedish population seems to have decreased in recent decades and is estimated at 11,000 pairs.

Memory artist

Nutcrackers store large numbers of hazelnuts in the moss within the territory. Neatly placed in two stores with a dozen or a score of nuts in each, they are carefully hidden and covered over with moss. These then provide the staple food through the winter and in addition food for the young during the following spring. If the supply is good, four eggs are

laid; if poor, only three and in really poor years few young survive. The birds can remember all their own hundreds of hiding-places and find them with great precision through a thick layer of snow. They never forget altogether which stores have been emptied, even if new snow has fallen and covered the signs. The previous year's caches, if any such still remain, can also be located if the current season's supplies have petered out. Furthermore, the stores are emptied in the correct order according to 'best-before date'. Swanberg considered that the memory was stored as a movement in the individual bird's space. If he himself hid hazelnuts while in sight of a Nutcracker it could not find them. I am inevitably led to think of how much easier it is to remember series of numbers if we form a picture of them, or words if at the same time we write them down with a hand movement. Nutcrackers also consume insects and take eggs and young of other small birds during the summer months.

Large eruptions

The Siberian cembra pine thrives in cold climates and has been planted in many places in parks and churchyards in Norrland. Nuts or seeds from its cones represent the most important food source for the Slender-billed Nutcrackers, *macrorhynchos*, which have become established locally in Norrland. Sweden's 'normal' Thick-billed Nutcracker, *caryocatactes*, is a pronounced resident which spends its entire life in its home territory. Sven Nilsson writes in *Skandinavisk fauna* that 'the area in which it has made its home it rarely leaves'. The juveniles however, may go on a wandering tour during late summer and autumn if the current year happens to produce a particularly poor hazelnut harvest.

Slender-billed Nutcrackers, on the other hand, can in some years undertake mass emigrations when the Siberian cembra pine's seed set is poor. It is such eruptions that have resulted in small populations having become established in, especially, north Sweden. Nilsson was very aware of these migrations, which he compared with those of lemmings, but he did not know where they came from. During years with influxes of Slender-billed Nutcrackers the general public usually becomes aware of this otherwise relatively discreet bird, which then often turns up in gardens, eats apples and visits feeding stations. If you wish to attract the

race macrorhynchos
race caryocatactes

Thick-billed Nutcracker to feeding places, these should be sited close to a spruce forest and provide just hazelnuts.

Nutcrackers are seen most easily in autumn during their provisioning trips to hazel stands in the district. The trips often begin as early as the end of August and reach a peak towards the end of September: in good years they may continue throughout the autumn. In flight against the sky, the bird looks dark with a whitish vent and surprisingly like a Jay thanks to its broad wings with spread fingertips. However, it is more front-heavy and long-billed and has a noticeably short tail. Beneath the tongue it has a special pocket which it fills with hazelnuts and this is why, on its return journey, it has a 'heavy' pouch under the chin. The rump is dark brown and the tail blackish with a broad white outer border, which is conspicuous when it takes off.

The Nutcracker's most common call is a simple metallic rolling '*ehrrrrrk*', with almost no vowel sound. It has a somewhat yelling but at the same time suggestive which ring carries a long distance; it can hardly be compared with that of any other bird. This species also has other, shorter, vowel-less rolling calls and an unobtrusive chattering song, whining and scraping.

Drop-shaped spots in the gloom of the spruce forest

At close range the Nutcracker is dark brown, strewn with pale drop-like spots. The blackish wings have a green shimmer. As an artist one can sometimes wonder at a certain colour marking, a wonder which easily turns into a number of questions on why this very one? What is the purpose?

There are about 120 corvid species in the world. The typical crows, the genus *Corvus*, seem to have restricted their plumage colours to the black-and-white scale. In other groups, such as the jays, there is a much bigger offering of colours where many have evolved blue shades and various attractive ochre, buff and grey colour ranges, sometimes combined with strong black-and-white contrasts. Few however, seem to have developed a pure brown colour as on the Nutcracker, except for a closely related sister-species in the Himalayas. The exception could be the Brown Jay *Cyanocorax morio* of Middle America. Closest in colour is the crown of the Siberian Jay, which has a distinctly brown tone. There are only three species of nutcracker in the world and the North

American Clark's Nutcracker *Nucifraga columbiana* is marked simply in grey, white and black. The pigment in black feathers consists of melanin, eumelanin and pheomelanin. Juvenile feathers in corvids have less of the blacker pheomelanin and can fade to an almost brown colour. Perhaps this is what has happened with the Nutcracker, which has, through evolution, reduced its blackest pigment in the body feathers and retained it in the black green-glossed wings. But why? When I recall the words of Swanberg I chance upon a number of his photographs of Nutcrackers incubating on their nests in the gloom of the spruce forest. The birds are sunk deep down in the nest, built from spruce twigs, next to the trunk. Snow still seems to be covering the ground and branches. In the nest, the pale spots on the brown ground colour suddenly become dead spruce twigs and the greyish mid-brown becomes spruce bark. The body appears to become an enlarged pixelated picture of a tangle of small branches and bark scales. Drop-shaped spots of this kind are typical of thrushes and flycatchers when very young and, in their case, it is obviously a way of avoiding detection. With the Nutcracker both sexes incubate and both brood the young. There, in the bitterly cold winter, they are well camouflaged with their drop-like spots.

race soemmerringii
immature
adult

JACKDAW

Corvus monedula

THE JACKDAW seems small, almost dainty, in comparison with the larger crows. It looks generally all dark in flight and the body is dark slate-grey. Wings and tail are blackish with a mauve or greenish gloss depending on the angle of the light. The nape has a beautiful silver-grey tone partially varying in lustre and a texture that gives it a well-groomed appearance. Contrasting with this are the black forehead and face, which together with pale greyish-white eyes give it an expression different from that of other corvids. The Jackdaw's captivating appearance with the pale silver-coloured eye and its voice have made it one of the more popular birds in the urban landscape. The eye of the very young juvenile is grey-blue, but changes to grey-brown when it is full-grown, only then to pale again to the peering silver eye. Just like the Hooded Crow, the Jackdaw retains the larger wing feathers through the first winter and in spring the young year-old birds can often be identified by their browner remiges. It is often a couple of years before the Jackdaw makes its first attempt to breed. Jackdaws vary somewhat in appearance geographically, and if one studies a flock it is often possible to distinguish individuals by differences in the paleness of the nape. Males are a little paler than females. Often the younger, year-old birds have not developed full 'silver-fox status'. Some birds have a pronounced paler patch on the side of the nape. This is a character which is more common farther east, in the race *soemmerringii*. It occurs also on birds which breed in Sweden, but is more frequent in wintering flocks.

Like most corvids, Jackdaws have an intricate social display which makes us, as humans, interested in them and also leads us to project our own peculiarities on to them. Sven Nilsson writes in *Skandinavisk fauna* that the Jackdaw 'becomes very tame and forms an attachment to the one who feeds and looks after it'. In the Scanian dialect the bird was called *alika*, and the expression *full som en alika*, meaning 'as drunk as

a Jackdaw', doubtless comes from the fact that people gave these tame Jackdaws bread steeped in alcohol in order to entertain their guests. The Jackdaws became inebriated by and even dependent on the alcohol.

Jackdaws form partnerships in the autumn, often as immatures and then live in pairs throughout their life. The noisy gatherings at dusk are a way of finding one's partner so that the two will be able to sleep close together. This is in fact what we often see in town and city trees in the winter, the Jackdaw pair perched closely side by side like a couple of new lovers. Within the flock there is a clear social order of rank and at the same time a strong unity around defending the members against intruders from outside. Jackdaws are for the most part residents in Sweden, even though more northeasterly populations migrate and, towards autumn, younger birds also move southwards. The population has increased in recent years and there are about 200,000 pairs of Jackdaws in the country. They readily visit birdtables and the Jackdaw usually makes around tenth place on the 'Winter birds on our doorstep' list.

Onomatopoeia

The Swedish name for the Jackdaw, *kaja*, pronounced 'ka-ya', is, as with most of the corvids, onomatopoeic. The species' 'kya' or 'ka' calls have a nice melodic ring which sounds like a form of address. When Jackdaws chat, the sounds are inflected with slightly different stress but always retain their special ring.

Jackdaws in Sweden breed both solitarily and colonially in cavities in trees and buildings bordering cultivated fields. In other parts of Europe they breed also in cliff crevices. Chimneys are very popular nesting sites, even though houseowners do not always like the flue being blocked. I have more than once taken care of sooty Jackdaw young which has come out into the living room. They seem then, from their coloration, to have been already prepared for life in a chimney flue. Chimneys are in many places the most important nesting sites. In woodland, the birds utilise hollow oaks and the old cavities made by Green and Black Woodpeckers.

Their predilection for thermals around large buildings, in other words artificial cliffs, is a well-known fact for those who live in cities. Jackdaws are elegant and acrobatic in the air, with long, slightly pointed wings. At signs of danger the whole flock can gather in dense formations which twist and turn like a shoal of fish across the sky. The great cathedrals which tower aloft in the lowlands, not uncommonly have thousands of Jackdaws which towards the evening meet for flight displays and social gathering. They roost in dense flocks both on buildings and in trees. In the morning they form smaller flocks which, with elegant and purposeful flight, move out in different directions towards the fields.

Generalist

Jackdaws are, together with Rooks, the most social of all corvids and the two species are often seen together on pastures and short-grass areas at places where the Rook also nests. Because of their differing bill sizes the two species rarely compete for food. The Jackdaw takes insects and larvae which live in the grass rather than in the upper layer of soil, in other words it picks its food, whereas the Rook digs or drills its out. When there are plenty of worms at the surface this is a food source which both utilise. Spilled grain and plant seeds are also an important part of the diet and they are often drawn in large flocks, along with other corvids, to temporary abundances of seeds on fields and around farmyards and silos. The Jackdaw is quite simply a generalist which can exploit not only cultivated land but also urban parklands and the inner city's discarded food remnants. It is not always so popular and sometimes, when the birds gather in flocks a thousand strong above a park or churchyard, they may be seen by many people as frightening or intimidating.

ROOK

Corvus frugilegus

THE ROOK is the size of a Hooded Crow but seems more slender in build, with a longer, more wedge-shaped bill and somewhat more 'loosely joined together' wings and tail. If you watch a Rook in light wind, it is often as if the feathers are lifted by the wind and the wing looks a little 'looser'. This creates interesting shadow effects for an artist, and Rooks are enjoyable subjects. Their featherless face adds a human characteristic and when seen from the front it resembles an old woman with a black head-scarf. Furthermore, Rooks have slightly longer and more bushy 'trousers' compared with other corvids. The Rook's black plumage has a wonderful gloss and lustre which make its wings look dull. The reflected colours are mainly bluish with an element of lilac and greenish-blue on the primaries and primary coverts. The long bill and the bare face are an adaptation to the bird's habit of probing in the ground with the bill and pulling up worms, beetles and larvae from the earth and loose ground litter. When it is cold and the ground freezes or the snow cover is too deep, the Rooks often resort to bird-feeding sites.

Urban steppe

In all likelihood Rooks originate from the vast steppe landscapes in the east and made their way westwards concurrently with the expansion of agriculture. The countryside in central Russia, in the regions around Omsk where I travelled to study gulls, consists of miles and miles of grasslands with endless groves of broadleaf trees. It is easy to imagine that this is the Rooks' original environment, just where woodland becomes pure steppe. In Sweden this species is tied to the extensive agricultural tracts and is quite happy on the outskirts of towns and small communities. Now the birds seem to be well at home in the urban environment. In Visby there has been a rookery since a couple of decades ago. It seems as if roundabouts, road areas, parks and all kinds of mown grass areas around buildings are its main haunt. Perhaps we could appoint the Rook as 'the roundabout bird'. The popular expression of people's art in decorating roundabouts with a home-made dog effigy came to an abrupt end when the Swedish cartoonist Lars Vilks stole the idea in 2007. In Scania however, there is no shortage of roundabouts and there too, they seem to be a favourite haunt of Rooks. I live so far out in the country that there are no roundabouts at all and the district's 'roundabout dog' had to stand at a T-junction. The Rook's partiality for roundabouts has fortunately not yet brought it any symbolic significance and the birds have quite simply adapted to a type of short-grass habitat that has increased in number while naturally grazed fields diminish. There are about 45,000 breeding pairs of Rooks in Scania and the entire Swedish population amounts to 48,000 pairs. The number has stabilised following substantial increases in earlier decades.

The Rook's social life

Rooks nest colonially in groups of tall trees usually situated close to villages and towns. Their social life, which takes place on a more open stage compared with other corvids, attracted attention from naturalists early on. The Rooks' apparently human virtues such as faithfulness to the breeding-colony trees, punctual appearances and noisy discussions about how the social life should be organised have drawn a number of English gentlemen to undertake detailed studies. The English ornithologist and bird-artist Franklin Coombs, himself a Rook specialist, wrote in his 1978 book *The Crows* about Lewis Harding, the pioneer in this field. In 1847 Harding was prescribed occupational therapy by a doctor for what today we call 'psychosocial problems'. He was to occupy himself with something which demanded absolute focus but which was neither strenuous nor stressful. He was therefore ordered to study a Rook colony every day of the year and to make detailed notes. This was perhaps the first in-depth study of bird behaviour.

During the winter, Rooks gather together with other corvids towards the evening at special roost sites, in trees, avenues or groves. Several different local Rook colonies and wintering populations then gather to roost communally and, in some places, such gatherings can consist of thousands of birds, up to 16,000 individuals having been noted. It is during nightfall, around the time when darkness sets in, when the pair-members must find each other and a place in the tree, that it is most noisy.

Rooks form pairs during the autumn and partners remain together for life. Since they nest so close together, it is important that pair-members, faced with the most intensive nest-building period, have strengthened their bonds so that they can defend their stick nest against the neighbours, which are not slow to steal twigs from an unguarded nest. When the Rooks return to their breeding colony towards late winter they are very noisy and fight intensely over the best nesting sites in the centre of the rookery.

Resident and migrant

The Rook is migratory in large parts of Russia and the Baltic countries and, with easterly winds, it comes in across southeast Sweden and can then turn up more or less anywhere. On Gotland this happens quite punctually in mid-October. In Scania it is now mostly a resident, but many from the more northerly populations migrate in autumn. In *Skandinavisk fauna*, in 1858, Sven Nilsson describes the Rook as a migrant which returns at the end of February. Presumably the species was a more pronounced migratory bird in earlier centuries when the climate was colder, during the so-called little ice age at the start of the 1400s up to Nilsson's time in the mid-1800s.

Song with a joy-filled heart

The Rook is noisy, especially near the nesting colony, where the sound level can sometimes be disturbingly high. The commonest call is a '*rraaahk*', which is clearer, straighter and more hollow than the crow's call. It varies in pitch, but has a particular ring which distinguishes it easily from a flock of crows. Since Rooks defend only a small area around the nest, the song has no territorial pretensions. The English describer of nature Gilbert White wrote to a friend in 1778 that Rooks, in the breeding season, attempt sometimes in the gaiety of their hearts to sing, but with no great success'. The song is a quiet chatter with guttural and creaking sounds. White was probably not completely right, but

young Rook

Rooks sing to attract females and younger, unpaired Rooks in particular, sing from a position outside the rookery and maybe the heart becomes filled with joy when one sings. Where corvids are concerned, we can be excused for such 'prohibited' anthropomorphism. In every study made we find many parallels between corvids' behaviour and that of humans.

Omnivore

The Rook is omnivorous, but largely dependent on earthworms to feed its young. Wet fields with short grass turf are therefore an important habitat for it and here the benefit of town-park management comes in, those who look after roundabouts and parks. Today's Rooks have less need than in the past to fly out into the cultivated fields to procure food. They accompany the general development which is increasingly moving in towards the towns. The extensive cultivated landscapes and pasture-lands are however, crucial for supporting large flocks of Rooks. The diet consists mostly of worms, cranefly larvae, beetles, corn grain and other crops. Large flocks work their way over the fields in a rolling movement such that all the time the birds finding themselves at the back fly forward to the front.

adult Carrion Crow

Young Rooks and Carrion Crows

Young Rooks do not develop the bare grey skin around the bill until their second summer. They can therefore be confused with the Carrion Crow, *Corvus corone*, which is an all-black relative of the Hooded Crow. The nearest breeding Carrion Crows to Sweden are in south Denmark and appear rarely in south Sweden and Norway; they are seen quite regularly in Scania. Young Rooks are more inclined to roam on their own, which is why they turn up often as solitary individuals among a group of Hooded Crows and can then easily create a certain confusion. In comparison with crows, a young Rook usually looks somewhat smaller, with a more pointed crown and the area around the bill-base looks somewhat different. The tuft of bristle-like feathers at the base of the upper mandible is more rounded, as if stuck on like a false moustache and the base of the lower mandible and corner of the bill are paler. The bill too, is slightly more pointed. Young Rooks retain their juvenile secondaries and primaries and greater secondary coverts, which creates a little contrast between the new black, more blue-glossed feathers and the more dull, brownish-black juvenile remiges. This is best seen diagonally from behind against the light. Towards spring this contrast usually increases and becomes easier to observe.

HOODED CROW

Corvus cornix

WHAT MORE CAN BE SAID OF THE HOODED CROW other than that it is grey and black, common and that everybody knows the crow. The wildlife-painter Bruno Liljefors liked crows as subjects and as company in the field. Perhaps it was his depictions of crows on fences in the Uppland landscape that found their way in to our picture of the wildlife of everyday Sweden. Liljefors painted many crows and gave his youngest daughter the name Kraka (close to the Swedish word for crow, *kråka*). In any case the crow seems to have secured a place rather deep in the Swedish soul. Maybe it is in reality the Ravens of Aesir, Thor's scouts Hugin and Munin, which through metempsychosis (transmigration of the soul) have come a bit closer to us, acquired a more benign and homely image, become Christian – mother's little crow. The crow is a symbol of a simple life on the land, in grey wadmal and black jacket on Sundays, the ultimate Smålander who walks across the field and gazes at the dark earth furrows, ingenious and loyal to his neighbourhood.

The grey crow

In 1859, Magnus von Wright described the Hooded Crow's grey colour as a 'beautiful light ash-grey'. It requires an inspired painter to pass such a judgement. I do not know of any poet who has expressed anything attractive about the Hooded Crow's grey colour. The colour range is like soot and ashes, plain and commonplace. It often seems a bit dirty grey, in some lights warm, perhaps earth-coated, in others colder steel-grey. At closer range one has a feeling that the grey feathers have a dark shaft streak. The grey colours fade somewhat with the sunlight and, when the birds are in moult, the old feathers look paler and more warm-toned, the new ones more neutral grey. We often perceive the bird as being dark

10.1.15
10.2.15

in general, whether it is perched in the treetops or in flight. Maybe on a bright summer day it can appear to be a beautiful grey, a little like the colour of thistle down, when perched on a post in a field of mature rye. The black wing has a navy-blue or bluish-mauve tone which becomes a dark green reflection on the primaries, primary coverts and alula. On cloudy days one is hard pushed to see any colour at all in the black. Young crows lack gloss on the flight-feathers and, in the spring of their second calendar-year, acquire an increasingly more brown tone on the wing feathers as the sun's rays become ever stronger.

Unusually grey

The fact that our crow is grey on the body is the most unusual thing about it, as most species in the genus are black. Our crow, too, occurs in all-black forms which are found throughout west and south-west Europe and in much of North Asia. Linnaeus in 1758 treated the black form as constituting the nominate race *corone*, which means 'crown' (both coronet and top of head) and the grey crow as the race *cornix*, which means simply 'crow'. The distributional border between the all-black Carrion Crow and the Hooded Crow runs through south Denmark, down through Germany towards the Alps, around the latter and includes also Italy and the countries east of there. The Hooded Crow is also found in Ireland and in northern Scotland. Whether these two forms are species or races has for a long time been the subject of discussions. The birds themselves select by preference a partner which looks the same as they do, which is why the border between the forms is maintained. Nevertheless, genetic drift between the populations is relatively substantial and hybrids occur in a narrow belt along the border line. Black crows in west Germany however, are genetically closer to Hooded Crows in east Germany than to the black crows which breed in southern France.

crow foot

All corvids of the genus *Corvus* are more or less omnivorous and have learnt to utilise what humans leave behind or discard around houses and gardens. The crow is strongly tied to villages and suburbs and farming areas and is found over the whole of Sweden where there are people living. It usually makes between fifteenth and twentieth place on the 'Winter birds on our doorstep' list. About 180,000 pairs of Hooded Crows breed in Sweden.

Winter crows

The crow is generally a resident, but in autumn crows migrate in to Sweden from breeding areas in Russia and then migrate back in the spring. It is therefore not certain that those crows which winter in a particular region also breed there. During the passage and winter periods it is usual for crows, Jackdaws and Rooks to gather in communal flocks which forage on fields and pastures and roost together in trees.

Where I live on Gotland, the crows are suspicious to the point of being shy of people. They are found everywhere in arable country and always seem to be present in winter as well as summer. Seldom do they stay where they are; however, if you appear interested in what they are doing and the distance is less than about 75 metres. It has to be winter proper and really cold before they venture forth to my feeding station. If I am myself in the studio, I have to take shelter behind cover or in some hide-out just behind the window if I wish to see them at closer range. I know that the crows are there quite often, but when I have driven my car into the courtyard they knew what was going on and they keep mostly at a safe distance. Presumably this is due to the fact that crows are still hunted here on the island. In Stockholm and, I suspect, in most other cities and towns, you have to chase off the crows immediately if you have left something valuable in the way of food outside the house. They quickly learn what to be on guard against and whom. We also have shore-living crows on the island which have specialised on what the sea offers.

The crows are what they eat, just as we are, though somewhat the other way around. In the cities the menu often consists of remnants of fast food from streets and market squares and young crows have been shown to have a lower weight when they leave the nest compared with those in the countryside. Nevertheless, the city crows seem to get along perfectly fine. In total however, the population has decreased in recent times, perhaps owing to the fact that there are no longer any open refuse tips and perhaps because of increased competition from Ravens out in the countryside.

Smart crows

Corvids are generally regarded as being intelligent birds and that is certainly true if we compare the family with some other groups of birds which have a more specialised diet. Behaviours resembling those of humans are generally considered to indicate intelligence, but that is always open to discussion. In any case, corvids have an unusually large brain in relation to their body size, a characteristic which they share with chimpanzees and dolphins. Birds which are omnivorous are usually more flexible and 'calculating' in their nature and corvids do seem to have specially developed cognitive faculties. Corvids can collaborate, know how to create tools and how to make use of them, see the difference between different people and they seem able to communicate experiences among themselves. It is always very interesting therefore to follow crows when they are searching for food or, even better, when they are engaged in time-killing or amusing themselves with various games. I have seen crows holding a branch and swinging, either with their claws or with the bill.

When a pair of crows has established itself in an area in order to start nesting, the birds are zealous defenders of their territory. On one occasion I had a male crow frantically attacking its own reflection in one of my windows. Not so smart, maybe? Ravens are said to be able to distinguish between their own reflection and that of others, but this crow obviously could not do that. But I accept that, even with crows, there are differences in intelligence. If any birdtables are present within a crow territory, one can expect it to be only the two members of the pair which visit the feeding station towards spring. Otherwise, the crow is perhaps the least social of the corvids, individuals rarely gathering together in dense flocks.

Characters

I have painted or drawn crows on innumerable occasions, but they still continue to surprise me with their various behaviours and expressions. When we tackle the task of understanding their various facial gestures, we are easily bewildered. A crow can have a flat crown, or a slightly raised and conical one, with the nape angular or sometimes fluffed up and almost rounded. The black on the hood seems sometimes to reach down over the nape but at other times not at all. If we wish to understand what is happening with the different feather tracts, how they are positioned, how they reflect the light and how the shadows fall and make some tracts all black and others lustrous, we have to study them in real life. The different postures and the shape of the feathers are expressions of the crow's mood, but crows seem to have a wide repertoire of feather expressions, so that it is seldom easy to interpret a crow. They seem to endlessly vary their expressions and, as a bird artist, one can never really make crows out. The feathers around the lore and immediately below the eye appear to remain deep black in any light and the eye usually stands out as paler than its surroundings. They also have a quite particular gait, slightly waddling and with the feet turned inwards. Their expressions are basically incomprehensible and abstract, but sufficiently distinct for one to be able to project one's own feelings on to them.

Carrion Crows

Interest in the Carrion Crow's appearance has followed fast on the heels of taxonomic discussions over whether it is a species or a race. The Carrion Crow is an exact copy of the Hooded Crow in shape and behaviour, with the sole difference that it is entirely black with a metallic sheen. Our own ingrained picture of the crow as grey and black makes us Swedes routinely see only Rooks in Paris or London. The solitary black 'Rook' which walks about in Hyde Park however, is almost always a Carrion Crow. Nevertheless, young Rooks which have not yet developed the bare grey skin around the bill base can be confusingly similar to these Carrion Crows (see page 227). But when a supposed Carrion Crow turns up in Sweden, the question of differences becomes more interesting. Hybrids between Carrion and Hooded Crows appear in Sweden, perhaps more commonly than pure Carrion Crows. They can sometimes be very similar to Carrion Crows but they give themselves away by the fact that some part of the body is not one hundred percent black.

Drips on a metal pipe

The crow's calls are well known, so we rarely ponder on how much they actually vary. The commonest is a slightly drawn-out '*ahrrrk*', repeated a few times at a fairly rapid rate. When they are perched and just feeling well, there is a more rounded, slightly more melodic ring in the throat: '*aauhrrk*'. They may give a barking '*kaoop, kaoop, kaoop*'. Crows not uncommonly appear to display or sing: they bow the head and pump out a series of more metallic ringing sounds which seem to be coming from a deeper source, more like drips on a metal pipe in some concrete basement, '*kla-aw*'. When they call, the pale blue nictitating membrane usually covers the eyes and they therefore look exceptionally excited. If a Sparrowhawk should turn up, the crows often mob it with dry creaky '*krrrrr*' calls. The tone in their warning calls corresponds to their own unease or alarm, a Goshawk usually eliciting an indignant yelling in a higher key, '*kreehk kreehk*'.

It can be worthwhile to get out into the countryside on a still morning and listen to the way the crows talk with one another.

RAVEN

Corvus corax

THE RAVEN is the largest of the corvids and also the largest of all the world's passerines. At a distance and in flight its size may not always be obvious and it can fleetingly be taken for a Rook or a Carrion Crow. It is however, as big as a Buzzard, with a wingspan of up to 1.5 metres. When Ravens are perched together with other corvids or a bird of prey, their size becomes obvious. A male often weighs well over a kilo and is twice as heavy as a crow. The bill, especially of the male, seems oversized. It is entirey black with a strong gloss and colour reflections of blue and mauve. In flight, it has proportionately longer and more pointed wings than the crow and a more wedge-shaped tail which give it a unique silhouette.

Perhaps the Raven does not belong at the ordinary birdtable where wild-bird seed and suetballs are on offer. Despite this, it is found on the 'Winter birds on our doorstep' list. I guess that no Raven has set foot in any residential garden or windowbox, but that it is supplementary food for birds of prey that has attracted Ravens, or alternatively that the occasional Rook has been taken for a Raven. Ravens readily help themselves to food that is put out, but are far too suspicious to go right up to the house to search for food. The species is now common in most parts, having earlier, in the middle of the last century, been a species seen mainly in Norrland and on the west coast. There are about 32,000 pairs in Sweden.

The Raven's vocal repertoire is not unlike that of the crow, but all calls have a specific 'Raven ring' which one easily learns to recognise. When flying past they often utter a '*krruap*', in which the vowels especially have a clearer ring. In display flight they give a short '*klong*' (with no 'r' sound) which carries a long distance. When agitated, they give hard '*krak-krak-krak*' calls.

The Raven's intelligence

The Raven is a central figure in nordic mythology and was known early on for its intelligence. To talk of intelligence or cognitive ability is difficult when it comes to birds. A common factor for those species of animal which we regard as having a certain intelligence is that they have a large brain in relation to their body weight. Birds derive from dinosaurs and have evolved over the course of 300 million years in parallel with mammals and anthropoid apes. The Raven is probably not unique when it comes to cognitive ability, but it shares many of its abilities with many other corvids. To be able to recognise oneself in a mirror is a capacity which, apart from humans, only elephants, dolphins, Ravens and chimpanzees possess. Ravens have an episodic planning faculty and they can see and work out how to solve a problem. They can pursue comfort, such as becoming reconciled with somebody they have quarrelled with. They can find their bearings well in a hierarchy, understand their role and manoeuvre in this political landscape in order to ascend in the hierarchy. All corvids can play, often complex games, and they constantly invent new games.

One late afternoon I was sitting and painting the few remaining Teals at my local bay. It was a grey December day and dusk descended over the landscape as early as four o'clock. I made a final check with the telescope across the open landscape out towards Faludden and discovered a pair of Ravens on a rock. I got the impression that they were done for the day, had abandoned any further foraging and were now joining together just to make the trip to a night-time roost inside the wood. The male was somewhat crouched when the female took a couple of steps forward and began to scratch, or delouse, him on the nape. He seemed to appreciate all this and after a while I saw how his large bill became heavier and slowly began to droop. Then she gave him a couple of pushes quite lightly beneath the bill, with her own, whereupon he came to and raised his head again. She continued and of course it was not long before his bill began to droop again. Then she became determined and brought the bill up again and inside myself I could hear her say – wake up! This time she was less gentle, more positive in her request. He then perched straight until she had finished and they both moved off eastwards towards Honngänna wood. Avian or human? The difference is unimportant, the similarities striking.

female autumn

STARLING

Sturnus vulgaris

THE STARLING is a migrant in the north and a bird which, ever since I was a child, I associate with early spring. Together with the first larks, the Starling was the true herald of spring in the southern suburbs of Stockholm when I was growing up in the 1960s. One day, perhaps the first mild day in March, three black short-tailed birds were seen in the top of an aspen or oak. Then, as now, they often nested under roof tiles and sought songposts near the nest. As the TV aerials rose up with their regular branchwork across the tiled roof of the terraced houses, they soon became the Starlings' natural music-stand. Now these lingering sprawling 'fish skeletons' on the roofs must have only that one purpose, as a perch for Starlings and Swallows. I wish that I had been able to say that I had kept the aerial for the sake of the Starlings, but TV dishes are also still in place, so there are unfortunately other reasons why the remnants of TV history have still not been released from chimneys and gableboards.

The Starling population decreased drastically over one or two decades from the start of the 1980s. Numbers have halved since 1975. Their role as harbinger of spring was to diminish when I moved to Gotland and other spring birds came into focus. The Starling is a short-distance migrant which in winter moves towards west Europe, where the frost normally does not seal off the enclosed pasturelands. There are around 640,000 pairs in Sweden and, generally speaking, they nest everywhere where there is cultivated land with open fields and grass areas.

Starlings form flocks immediately after fledging and then move over wide areas. We often find that they have moved away from the region as early as June. The juveniles have often not completed their moult before October and the actual migration to the winter quarters usually takes place in October and the first half of November. Many of the Swedish Starlings migrate across to Britain during the winter.

In autumn Starlings readily eat fruit and berries, but they also look for beetles and other insects on fields so long as these are frost-free. A few choose to attempt overwintering in Sweden.

During the years when the 'Winter birds on our doorstep' survey was operating, the number of Starlings reported at feeding sites varied from a couple of hundreds to a couple of thousands. At my place in south Gotland, I often see a few which look as if they have overwintered and they readily seek out the last remaining winter apples in gardens. If it gets really cold they make for the shore and forage in the seaweed. Down in the seaweed, bacteria which break down other organisms create a warmer microclimate and this is alive with insects and crustaceans even if the air temperature is several degrees below zero.

When Blackbirds and Bullfinches fluff up their plumage to insulate themselves against the cold, they of course look rotund, as if they are trying out the down jacket in preparation for the nordic winter cold. The Starling, on the other hand, looks a little uncomfortable when the weather gets really cold and snowy. It is used to British winters.

The Starling's look

The Starling has a particular look, with the eye situated below the bill, or almost so. It is positioned exactly level with the corner of the bill base. The reason is that the Starling pokes the wedge-shaped bill down in the ground or the seaweed and then opens it so that a small peep-hole is created, the eye is then perfectly in line with the bill aperture. If you go out in the fields in spring or to the banks of seaweed in the summer, you can see that the surface is often perforated with such spy-holes. Starlings are in many ways nomads, which accompany or move with the food sources. In the spring when they arrive, it is worms and insects in the damp turf that are the main food. When the young leave the nest, it is caterpillars in the dense foliage that are important and then, during summer, the grasshoppers, butterflies and winged ants of the grasslands. In autumn they consume many berries and fruits and in winter in England it is again worms and beetles that make up the staple food.

The feather dress

Unlike the thrushes, young Starlings replace the entire juvenile plumage, including the remiges and rectrices. Young and adult Starlings are therefore very similar after October and the Starling flocks appear homogeneous in late autumn. At close range however, the young ones can often be separated by the appearance of the flank spots. The adults have pointed spots each penetrated by a small dark shaft streak, whereas the younger ones have slightly bigger, more heart-shaped and less sharp spots. This character is not always easy to see in the field, but sometimes the young retain an odd secondary and they often still have uniformly brownish-buff feathers throughout September, especially on the head.

The adult males have very narrow and pointed throat feathers with a more intense bluish-mauve gloss. There is almost no room for the spots at the tips of the feathers and they look more like small dots than those on younger birds and females. The young females in their first-winter plumage often have broader, more rounded buff fringes on the upper-parts and, in particular, the rump often looks entirely brownish-buff. The bill is mostly blackish in autumn and winter, but gradually becomes paler as spring approaches.

When they return to our latitudes there is not uncommonly a setback in the weather and it is most often then, in March, that I see Starlings at the birdtable. They often still have much of the white sequin-like spots, but the males quickly lose these and acquire their oily glossy plumage. In spring the males have a yellow bill with a blue-grey base, the females a mostly yellow bill with a pink base and a small dark tip. Females can have a paler brown or reddish-grey ring in the iris which makes them look somewhat meaner or glassy-eyed. The difference in iris colour means that the sexes can be separated at close range even during autumn and winter.

Squeaking and mimicking

Starlings will sing throughout the year and they are heard not uncommonly on fine autumn days, softly chattering from the top of a tree. Their varied song with imitated calls and its own creaking and squeaking sounds seems to be coming from more than one throat. The Starling is an orchestra on its own: it plays little melodies, often imitations of Curlews or Common Gulls, on the violin and accompanies itself with creaking and clicking sounds and measured rings from the triangle.

The Starling's character is rather like its outward appearance, sharp and energetic and when a flock attacks a fruit tree or fallen apples they all appear to be going at high revs, eating and calling at the same time. They often drive away thrushes with a rapid and distinct 'jab'. If a Sparrowhawk or other danger is detected, one member of the flock gives a few rapid '*pitt*' calls and in the same second the flock falls silent and takes wing.

the white spots on the flank on young female and adult female

female
male winter

HOUSE SPARROW

Passer domesticus

THE HOUSE SPARROW is intimately associated with man's habitations and the species has accompanied humans and agriculture up through Europe. It nests by and large everywhere where there are humans living, right up to the Arctic Ocean. The species was considerably more numerous when animal husbandry was more widespread and most farms had a diversified agriculture. In the towns and cities the House Sparrow did best when the horse was the principal means of transport. The ever more intensive and specialised farming and the amalgamating of farms have gradually reduced the number of places which can feed House Sparrows. It requires there to be animals in the farmyard which create warmth in cow-sheds, plenty of insects and crops which produce seed in winter. In the towns, feeding and food remains are presumably an important prerequisite. There are still however, about 450,000 pairs of House Sparrows in Sweden, half in the towns and villages and half around farms. This can be compared with the number of pairs of Chaffinches, which is estimated at more than 8 million. Despite this, many who live in more urban environments see the House Sparrow as being the 'most common' bird as it is locally still common and hops around cafe tables in the summer.

The House Sparrow's scientific name associates it with the simple and ordinary life. Certainly it prefers to eat crumbs from the rich man's table and undigested grain from horse-droppings and it is therefore easy to project human qualities on to this bird. The House Sparrow is extraordinarily fond of its home and seldom moves more than a couple of hundred metres from the farmyard or the house where it lives, perhaps somewhat farther if there is a bountiful supply of food there. So, one seldom comes across the House Sparrow far out in the cultivated landscape or at a feeding site where there are not any breeding sparrows in the vicinity. At my studio I see the occasional House Sparrow only rarely

although they occur in large numbers around the farmhouse where I live, which is perhaps a kilometre away. They would rather stay at home at the farm. Juveniles however, may move about during their first year of life. House Sparrows normally have at least two broods, often three, in any one year. One can therefore see moulting House Sparrows well into October. They nest mainly in cavities in buildings and beneath roof tiles, but locally in Europe they may build open nests in dense bushes.

The House Sparrow's plumage

On closer inspection on a nice June day, a male House Sparrow is a colourful bird with intense liver-brown, steel-grey and rust-red colours. With his black lores and entire breast and his contrasting white cheeks, he could certainly be described as a beautiful sparrow. The female has a more subdued pattern in various shades of sepia, grey and buff.

When we encounter House Sparrows in winter however, the situation is somewhat reversed. During late summer and early autumn the House Sparrows moult and the more contrasting and brighter colours of the male are concealed beneath light grey or buff fringes. The basic markings are there but all contrasts have been somewhat softened, even though the wings are, if anything, brighter in colour but with broader pale fringes. The black at the front is confined to the lore and a small patch under the bill. The bill becomes straw-yellow or greyish-yellow after the breeding season, but regains its black colour towards late winter. The liver-brown band over the temples and rearwards acquires a buffy marking centrally in the winter. In early summer the neck-collar and cheek are shining white anteriorly against the grey of the ear-coverts, but in winter this contrast is concealed beneath the feather fringes, especially on younger males. Since the birds of the year moult out all juvenile feathers, it is difficult to see any difference between young males and older males during the winter. I fancy however, that I see the older males to be more brightly marked on the head, blacker on the lore, more of the chestnut-brown is visible and the crown is purer grey. But I have not made any systematic study of whether it is generally possible to identify males in their first winter. In any case, a variation in males in winter can be seen whereby some are distinctly marked while others, probably

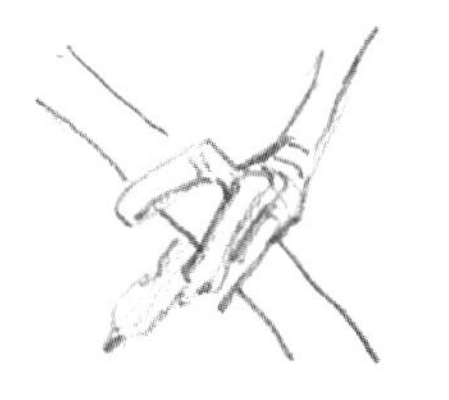

male, spring

first-winter males, show less contrast in the plumage. In the autumn the young ones have a more 'untainted' bill with softer colour tones, whereas the bill of older males looks a little more used, a little more unpolished. The black bib of males becomes gradually more apparent during the spring and is most distinct in mid-summer. With females I cannot see any age differences, but they can be individually different in the face, some having for example darker grey cheeks while others are pale buff-grey. The female has a soft, attractive face and the entire plumage has fine shades of buff and grey-brown.

Conversation in the honeysuckle

My regular objects of study live under the roof tiles on our workshop and have a honeysuckle bush as a living-room. This bush is their castle: the day begins there with a gathering at dawn before the work starts on the farm, intense meetings take place there during the day and the group gathers there before the night's repose. The discussions are always lively, but more so in the late winter and spring. Trying to write down and interpret their repertoire is not entirely easy and in most cases one takes little notice of whether it is a mixture of Tree Sparrows and House Sparrows in a given bush, which is not unusual. Essentially, we can say that these species sit and 'chirp' but that very description best fits the Tree Sparrow. House Sparrows 'bicker' rather than 'chirp'. Their conversational calls are variations on a single theme: '*cheip, chip-ip, kurr-chip, cheev*' and so on. Sometimes they give a more indrawn '*tziep*' like the Tree Sparrow. When quarrelling or perhaps in general excitement they give a chattering staccato. Sometimes a somewhat different '*wip*' is heard. The conversation often begins quite calmly, only to intensify somewhat and it seems as if there is some quarrelling over perches when they start their staccato chattering. The group can quite suddenly fall silent and then it is probably something which one of them considered to be dangerous, or else they are reacting to some unconfirmed 'rumour'.

House Sparrows and Tree Sparrows always have one or more thick shrubberies which they use as cover and as a meeting place. Usually they fly rapidly and directly when they are on their way to a feeding place and when returning they often come at great speed and plunge headlong into the bushes. If you play games with them a little, in other words if you imitate a grating alarm call, they hop around inquisitively within the bush and try to find a good gap through which to look out at the danger.

Ingenious opportunist

The diet consists of seeds from plants and grasses, corn grains on fields and spilled seed around barnyards and also food remnants from cafes and restaurants in towns and cities. This species also eats green leaves, flower buds and all kinds of fruit, such as currants, apples and pears. In the summer the young are fed initially with insects and spiders. They are also great consumers of aphids, which should please every gardener. The House Sparrow is adaptable and seems able to employ a number of different techniques to find food and, not uncommonly, it is seen inside apparently closed buildings. On rooftops it often looks for spiders and insects and it sometimes attempts to catch insects in flight.

male, winter

winter

TREE SPARROW

Passer montanus

MOST PEOPLE WHO ARE not much interested in birds usually have difficulty in distinguishing House Sparrow and Tree Sparrow, if they even care. The species are at first glance alike in both appearance and behaviour. If you point out to a novice the Tree Sparrow's black cheek patch and uniformly coloured reddish-brown crown, it is often an eye-opener. It can even whet the appetite for further bird-watching. With the Tree Sparrow the sexes are alike. It appears to be a touch smaller than the House Sparrow and generally tends more towards buff and red-brown and the belly sides are buff, never greyish as on the House Sparrow male. As with the House Sparrow, the bill colour changes after the breeding season. The Tree Sparrow however, acquires yellowish only at the base, the outer part of the bill remaining black. Any radical changes through the loss of feather fringes as with the House Sparrow male are non-existent with the Tree Sparrow. The breast remains pale and it never acquires the House Sparrow's big black breast patch. The Tree Sparrow has a thin white neck-collar which is interrupted on the nape, where the brown colour of the crown joins with the mantle. At the lower edge of the collar there is a small dark-spotted border, like a fringe, which is not directly visible other than when the bird stretches. The dark cheek patch can vary a little in size and sometimes it almost meets the brown nape feathers. The juvenile differs from the adults in having some of the features of House Sparrow and the crown is grey centrally and can give the feel of a hybrid between the two species. The cheek patch and bib are dirty brown. Such birds however, usually are not seen in winter but again, as with the House Sparrow, the moult can continue into October.

Common at the birdtable

The Tree Sparrow is more of a country-dweller compared with the House Sparrow. It thrives in agricultural country but also in villages and towns with gardens and parks, though it avoids the wholly built-up city. In addition, it is a little more mobile and Tree Sparrows often make excursions a fair way off from their nesting sites. They therefore find out if there is any new feeding site in the vicinity more quickly than their relative the House Sparrow, which is more stationary. The Tree Sparrow is however, a pronounced resident.

Its particular liking for gardens and houses and its marked seed diet mean that it is one of the three most common birds at the birdtable. During the 2015 'Winter birds on our doorstep' survey, 125,000 Tree Sparrows were counted and reported. The number of breeding pairs is estimated at 420,000. A large proportion of the stock therefore, visits feeding stations. I often have a hundred or so at my feeders and at times they can seem a little aggressive. They often perch at the big seed-dispenser and flick away seeds in order to get at the one they most prefer. Corn and sunflower seeds, among others, fall to the ground and they seem to prefer smaller seeds of plants such as hemp and millet. They like also to cling to the suetballs and when two or three Tree Sparrows have parked themselves there none of the tits will visit. It takes a Jay or a Great Spotted Woodpecker to drive them off. In the countryside, during spring and the breeding season, it is largely insects and caterpillars that constitute food for the young. Tree Sparrows often make their way out to neighbouring fields, abandoned workings or shores in order to feast on seeds from oraches and other plants.

spring

late winter

Chipping calls

The calls of the Tree Sparrow and the House Sparrow are quite similar to each other. Since both are common, one seldom has any reason to try to separate the species by the call. If you have one species in the garden hedge but not the other, it is probably difficult to distinguish a Tree Sparrow from a host of House Sparrows and vice versa. If you stand and deliberately listen to Tree Sparrows however, they have a somewhat different pitch or character. The Tree Sparrow has a slightly clearer, more 'chipping' call, usually in the form of '*chip, chep*' or sometimes '*chulp*'. Not uncommonly a rhythmic '*chipp...chulp*' is heard, unlike the House Sparrow's '*cheip*'. It also has a slightly more indrawn '*tziep*'. When more committed, Tree Sparrows utter a doubled 'chett-ett'. The Tree Sparrow's 'scold' or staccato is less chattering, harder and metallic: '*chett-ett-ett-ett-ett-ett*'. In flight a '*kiipp kiip*' or '*chett-tett*' is heard. I can imagine that somebody else's ear may interpret the Tree Sparrow's chattering quite differently, but there is an audible difference between these two species. Listening to Tree Sparrows is, if nothing else, a quite relaxing occupation.

Bofink 13/1 2012
Första vintern

CHAFFINCH

Fringilla coelebs

THE CHAFFINCH which we see at the birdtables in the winter is hardly recognisable as the richly coloured, obvious and extrovert Chaffinch which meets us in the April woodland. In winter the Chaffinches often move about more unobtrusively a bit outside the centre of events, quietly hopping about, looking for occasional seeds which have blown away or been discarded by the Tree Sparrows. At the seed-dispenser's perches or rim it is cocky Tree Sparrows or unruly Greenfinches that contend for the best places. It seems as if the Chaffinches work methodically one by one and avoid the crowd in the middle of the market-place. For anybody who is not accustomed to looking at birds they can easily escape notice.

Most of those which overwinter in Sweden are males and it is mostly younger males that stay behind. These young males in their first-winter plumage differ appreciably from the spring birds encountered in April or May. They are more like females, because more light rusty-coloured and brownish-buff fringes conceal part of the lovely colours which characterise Chaffinches in spring. The older males also have a winter plumage that is less bright in its colours. The spring plumage is produced by the wearing-off of the fringes. The purpose of the bird's colours in winter plumage is to give it more camouflage against the ground's range of colours during migration and at the wintering sites. The blue-grey crown and nape acquire a dusting of buff, the black forehead patch is concealed and the cold brownish-pink breast has a lighter, more buff tone. On the crown of younger males are two brown bands as on females and the chestnut-brown mantle colour has partly faded into buffy-brown tones. Younger males can sometimes be almost female-like, but they always have a more brownish-pink coloration than the females. The bill in winter is light buffy pink with only the extreme tip dark. Towards spring, in March, it becomes grey-blue with a black tip. If over the winter you have been feeding one or more young Chaffinches which perhaps hatched farther north and one day suddenly get a visit from returning locally breeding males in full nuptial trappings, the difference can be striking.

Sweden's second most common bird

The Chaffinch is, after the Willow Warbler, the second most common bird in Sweden and well known to most people. The population is estimated at 8.5 million pairs. We like to see it as a spring bird whose arrival coincides with the flowering of the blue anemone or liverleaf. These are often the first spring birds to fill the wood with daytime song; they bring the winter wood back to life.

This is mainly a migratory bird in the north. The large passage movements out of the country head southwest during October. Swedish birds winter mainly in west Europe and many get to England. Finnish birds seldom reach England but are more concentrated in southwest France; however, they winter in a wide corridor from south Sweden down to the Iberian Peninsula. The few which remain in Sweden often resort to birdtables, especially if it becomes cold and with the ground snow-covered. The largest number of winterers are found in the extreme south and southwest regions. In Scania and Halland this species is common in winter at birdtables. Where I live, in south Gotland, it is also regular with perhaps five or at times ten individuals.

A rewarding subject

The Chaffinch is a bird which I have painted relatively often. In spring plumage the males can compete for the position as one of the most attractive Swedish bird species. In autumn and winter they have a range of sophisticated markings and shades which inspire me to paint. Now and then I have set aside some time to look at females, especially in autumn, and found a little beauty among Sweden's birds which I had earlier not quite fully realised how to appreciate. The females correspondingly have other colour changes in the autumn, but they differ very little from the plumage which we are used to seeing in the spring: brown, buff and grey, as well as the wing's more contrasting blackish-brown, white and yellow

female winter
old male winter

tones. As so often, the autumn plumage is richer in shades, small tinges and soft transitions. In spring, when the feathers are more worn, these small tints disappear. At one time I was almost obsessed with reading off and interpreting these nuances in female Chaffinches, there was something about the face and the head that appealed to me and frustrated me. On the head a number of finely tuned buff tones, perhaps brownish-buff and light whitish-buff, was assembled. On the throat they have a pale patch which is framed below by a slightly darker border and then pale again at the neck base before the more soft grey-buff breast. Small finely marked transitions which could be seen only in a certain light under a cloudy sky – preferably on one of south Gotland's sandy fields so that the brownish-grey tones acquired a colour-defined background, so that the eye would be able to interpret it. I imagined sands in various colour tones which are running out and forming delicate patterns with perfectly regular transitions. A watercolour still waiting to be done.

The Chaffinch has in the Brambling a sister-species with tremendously similar shape and forms. The Chaffinch is possibly a little smaller and with a somewhat smaller bill. In mixed flocks in autumn the females of the two species can easily appear alike, but the Brambling always has a white 'slit' on the rump which is visible when the birds take off. It also has a more orange or ochre coloration and a yellower bill with a distinct dark tip. Characteristic of the Brambling is that the dark crown-stripes which continue down over the nape are more contrasting and sharply defined. In addition, the Brambling has a small splash of drop-shaped spots on the flanks which the Chaffinch always lacks.

Brambling, female

Chaffinch, female

Chaffinch, male first winter

BRAMBLING

Fringilla montifringilla

FOR THOSE OF US who regularly put out food and look out of the window with great enthusiasm, there is an informal order of rank among the bird visitors. Put simply, the more uncommon the species, the higher it is ranked. I have never investigated this among colleagues or read that many people think just like this; it is more a gut feeling and a certain insight into how we ornithologists think. Of course, no definitive list of rankings exists; it has to be seen more as a personal experience dependent on which part of the country and which habitat one has one's feeding station in. The most common, most commonplace species do not cause any eyebrows to be raised. But every time the eye looks out at the feeding place there is a small hope that a more uncommon species will turn up, perhaps a Common Redpoll among the Siskins or a Goldfinch. It does not need to be something very striking or remarkable, but variety is the spice of life, the whole time creating a sort of suspense around this type of watching, just as with all other watching. The list of species in 'Winter birds on our doorstep' has over the years been headed by Great Tit, Tree Sparrow, Blue Tit, Yellowhammer, Bullfinch, Blackbird, Greenfinch, Magpie and so on and this list serves well as a starting point, though in the reverse order.

For this reason a Redwing becomes more enjoyable than a Blackbird, a Hawfinch more exciting than a Greenfinch. The Brambling, which often ends up between tenth and fifteenth place, is a little more enticing than a Chaffinch, perhaps only for the reason that it does not breed in south Sweden but is a winter visitor there, despite the fact that in many years it comes before the Chaffinch in numbers seen at Swedish birdtables. The Brambling and the Chaffinch in addition form a species-pair, the differences and similarities between them being of interest from a number of different perspectives. All this is of course a matter for the individual but, depending on which species one normally has on the doorstep, there are gradations of observations and certain species create a little extra interest. The Brambling is one such species which, despite being relatively common at winter feeding stations, is noted and seen. I myself live in a migration corridor from mainly Finland and west Russia, where Bramblings migrate past in October and, on their return journey, in April. In October they are in perfect winter plumage and it is then a joy to watch them. I am fascinated by their fantastic patterns and colour range, like a bunch of autumn leaves in various brown, orange and yellow colours.

The autumn leaves' colour scale is presumably also the evolutionary explanation for these birds' winter plumage. It has evolved so that the bird will be able to perch unseen on the beech woods' floor of fallen leaves. Bramblings are in winter under the control of the beech's seed set. If there is plenty of food in Scania they remain, otherwise they move farther down to mainland Europe and in some years can end up right down in south Europe. In places with good supplies they can gather in enormous flocks for roosting. One flock in Switzerland which was flying to a roosting site was estimated at 70 million birds. On autumn migration they readily mix with Chaffinches and appear on agricultural ground, where they consume the stubblefields' spilled grain, maize and rape seeds, or simply weed seeds. Seeds from, for example, Swedish whitebeam and rowan are also taken. The Bramblings which winter in Sweden are concentrated in the southernmost regions, where there are large numbers of beech trees. The number overwintering can however, change from hundreds of thousands to just a few thousands, all depending on the supply of beechmast. Even in years with few Bramblings in Sweden, this is a bird which can turn up in winter in all types of country.

Bitter orange and nectarines

During the breeding season the Brambling male is a bird rich in contrasts, with a raven-black head and back, orange-yellow breast and shoulders and a black-and-white wing pattern, an out-and-out signal to conspecifics. At the same time, if you put it in a mountain birch forest with white tree trunks and black branches and black lichens, the picture becomes a different one; then it can both be a signal flag and be well camouflaged. Before they leave their birch forests in the north the Bramblings moult. The males then take on a completely different appearance. All black areas at the front and on the back are concealed by long ochre-coloured or grey fringes. The older males can show a black mask around the eye, but on the younger males hardly any black at all is visible on the head. Younger males have instead adopted a female-like head pattern with darker bands over the crown and down over the nape and a grey neck side. The warm-coloured parts on the breast, the shoulders and the wing-feather fringes have a succession of saturated orange or brownish-orange tones. On the wing, the outer webs of the flight-feathers are bright yellow.

The pale fringes remain until well into the late winter. At a certain point, when the sun and wear have made the fringes brittle, they are broken off. How much black shows through from the beginning or how fast the fringe loss proceeds depends partly on the individual and partly on how much ultra-violet radiation the feather is exposed to. When the pale outer part, the fringe, is broken off, this happens immediately outside the black part of the feather and leaves behind some pale marking. During the spring migration in April a few are already entirely black on the head and mantle, but most are still piebald and have a yellow bill. The final pale parts then fall off at the start of May and the bill becomes black. If you come across a full-coloured Brambling in the middle of May it is a surprising experience, as it is rich in contrasts, like a Pied Flycatcher with an orange-coloured breast. The bill is black in summer and in winter yellow like a maize kernel with a diffusely darker tip. The yellow bill with its dark tip is often a conspicuous character when Bramblings are hopping around among other finches and buntings.

The female has, as with the Chaffinch, a more toned-down plumage and the brighter rusty-orange colours have been replaced by a somewhat duller colour range, like dried bitter-orange peel and dried nectarines. Females and young males have a particular marking around the eye which gives them a pleasing facial expression which is easily noticed. The black eye is framed by a pale cream-coloured area and nearest the eye there is a paler eyering which is broken by a black spot, a beauty spot. In front of the eye there is a dark area, shown by many birds, the purpose of which is to reduce the reflection of light into the eye. The function of the beauty spot we can but wonder over, I am sure and the only function I can imagine is that it breaks up the eye's shape and that it can perhaps improve the camouflage when the female is incubating deep in the nest and only the head is protruding. It is very pretty, in any case.

The bird of the upland birch forest

We may wonder how evolution works when these colour scales come washing in. The Chaffinch which goes for the cold pink, wine-red, brown and grey-blue with green on the rump, is this an adaptation to the colour scale of the temperate forests while the Brambling has been painted by the upland birch forest? Black, white and on the ground last year's yellow and brownish-yellow birch leaves melt through. During the quaternary, the last 2.6 million years, the dominating glacial periods have isolated the two species from each other. When the last inland ice across Scandinavia melted away, the Brambling came in from the east behind the ice and the Chaffinch came from the south. They now meet in Norrland, where one species is gradually replacing the other. The Chaffinch is found far up and into Norrland's hinterland but the numbers thin out towards the mountain chain, where the Brambling takes over. The densities of Brambling increase the nearer we come to the mountain chain and are at their greatest in the upland birch forest.

The Brambling is not site-faithful but more of a nomad. In the same way as the wintering areas are governed by beechmast, so breeding is dictated by the occurrence of larvae of the autumnal moth, *Epirrita autumnata*. Its presence in an area can therefore vary appreciably from one year to another. It is estimated that on average two million pairs of Bramblings breed in Sweden.

Perhaps it is all this that makes me give the Brambling a slightly higher ranking than the Chaffinch at the birdtable: the irregular appearance, the character of a nomad, the unexpected design, the sudden transformation, the winter coat which is cast off, entrance in black hood and cloak. Or is it only the early teenager's dreams of northern expeditions in Lapland coming to the surface, which are reborn every time I see a Brambling? In nature-photographer Svante Lundgren's *Stiglost land* ('Trackless country') from 1946, there is a black-and-white photograph of a pair of Bramblings, near the nest in a fork in a downy birch. The route there went via the Lainia river, in a 'territory with no roads, full of bogs and morasses', where the dreams are awakened.

young female winter
old male spring
old male winter
young male winter

GREENFINCH

Chloris chloris

THE GREENFINCH is one of Sweden's most common birds and it prefers to nest around buildings. There is probably not one arbor vitae or spruce hedge in south and central Sweden which has not at some time housed a Greenfinch nest. Despite this, I find it to be a bit of an anonymous figure. Nobody seems to talk spontaneously about the Greenfinch. Why I do not know, but perhaps we see it as a little ordinary and mossy in coloration and it hardly stands out at the winter birdtable; Greenfinches are sociable to the degree that they almost disappear between cheeky Blue Tits and chattering Tree Sparrows. It is mostly the bright yellow edges along the wing that draw the eye to it. Even the powerful and intense song seems to pass unheard when it is delivered from the top of a birch or spruce high above the roofs in the residential districts in spring.

The Greenfinch winters throughout the country and can be seen at feeding stations over the whole of the north, even high up towards the Arctic Ocean coasts, but it is probably dependent on artificial feeding in order to survive right up in the north. After 2008 the Greenfinch was threatened by the parasitic disease known as canker and its numbers were severely reduced at the start of the second decade of the present century. Keeping seed-dispensers and birdtables clean is an important measure to reduce the spread of the disease.

Linnaeus's thistle-finch

Earlier the Greenfinch was placed in the genus *Carduelis*, which alludes to the thistle, *carduus* in Latin. Linnaeus gave the name 'Thistle-finch', *Fringilla carduelis*, to the Goldfinch and the epithet has since been the generic name for several species of finch which eat seeds. At one time the Greenfinch was included in that genus, but today it has been afforded a genus of its own, *Chloris*, which comes from the Greek *chloros*, which refers to a light yellowish-green colour and is associated with young greenery. Chloris is also the name for the Greek nymph who represents the spring. When the first signs of spring are seen in Greece and around the Mediterranean countries in February, their Greenfinches are considerably more bright yellow-green than the Greenfinches which visit our seed-dispensers in the far north. When I look out at my quite drab grey finches in November the Elysian nymphs feel very distant. If the females had been given the name of the species, it could just as well have been called brownfinch or greyfinch.

Unskilled labourer in green

The Greenfinch could be described, a little irreverently, as the unskilled labourer of the winter bird fauna. It is robust and looks muscular, with a sculptural body, big cheeks, slightly stern facial expression, small eyes and rather heavy pale red feet. The bill is large, almost ungainly, and adapted to enable working slightly bigger and harder seeds. When the birds methodically work sunflower seeds, it is not unusual to see other birds hopping after and taking the fragments.

The green colour tints of the males are elusive like the mosses of the forest and seem constantly to vary with the light and the seasons of the year. Individual variation is marked. Not until the oaks begin to come into leaf at our latitudes have the Greenfinches worn off their rough coat and can dazzle us in their true spring apparel. They undergo loss of feather fringes, even though this is not so obvious as with, for example, the Brambling. The new body feathers that grow in during the autumn have a greyish or grey-brown fringe which conceals or tones down the brighter green colours. The Greenfinches which lead a dull life out in the weed fields in autumn are quite unlike the handsomely green-and-yellow males which we see when the trees are coming into leaf. The sharper April light certainly plays its part too. In May, when the greenery and the newly arrived spring birds have already stolen all our attention, the more exotic Greenfinch males barely receive the attention which they deserve.

The male has a bright yellow colour on the belly, something which the winter snow and the returning light in February can reveal. When

the birds are on the ground however, the belly and the colour are in shadow and the details vanish. The purpose of the bright yellow belly is that it should stand out in the low morning sun when the male performs his song flight. Then his bright yellow wingpanel and tail base also are conspicuous and he becomes like a male brimstone butterfly in the March sun when he flies in wide circles on slow-cranking wings. On the perched bird the yellow outer web of the primaries forms a bright yellow band. Often the yellow continues along the front edge of the wing and here we can see a difference between immature and adult birds. On adult males the longest feather in the 'thumb area' of the hand, the alula, is almost wholly yellow on the outer web, with an ash-grey tip, whereas on young males it has more dark and olive-green shades.

The outer tail feathers have a bright yellow outer web which is often concealed when the bird is perched on the ground but becomes a distinct signal to the group's members when the flock rises at a sign of danger. The bill is mostly light horn-coloured, though I fancy that I can see a certain difference in bill colour across the seasons. In autumn the bill is more greyish-pink with a darker culmen and tip, while in spring it

young male

adult female, grey

adult female, brown

seems to become more light buffish-pink as if faded. Perhaps this is due to a difference in food choice, or else it is a real change governed by hormones as with the Hawfinch and Chaffinch. With the Greenfinch the transformation is in that case the reverse: it goes from darker to paler.

For somebody with the time and interest and nothing else to do on a winter's day, it is possible to devote much time to separating the individual birds. The Greenfinch is, like many other birds, a creature of habit and, if an individual has chosen to work its sunflower seed on a particular branch, the chances that it will return to the same place are high.

Golden-green against grey

I do not know how many hours I have studied Greenfinches at my feeding station. At first sight males and females can look very similar to each other, but the more one studies them the more variation one discovers. The difference between males and females is normally quite obvious, but disparities are found even within the respective sexes. Initially I thought that the differences which I observed were dependent on age and I therefore tried to categorise them into just first-winter plumage and adult birds. This soon proved to be a delicate task. The only certain way in which one can age Greenfinches is to see if they have any juvenile feathers, mainly wing and tail feathers, remaining in the plumage. All Greenfinches replace the body feathers after the breeding season and the adults replace the whole set of wing and tail feathers while the young birds at our latitudes normally retain most of these. The Greenfinch often has two broods, sometimes three. The birds which have already fledged in May have, of course, advanced farther in their development than those which made their first flight in August. We can therefore see hugely different degrees of wear in the juvenile feathers and also in the extent to which they have changed individual feathers in tail and wing. Early-hatched young sometimes have very worn, pointed and brownish tail feathers which clearly differ from the adults' more rounded and greyish-black ones. More than half of my Gotland Greenfinches have replaced the odd tail feather and two or more usually all three tertials. Attempting to age Greenfinches during the winter months is therefore often tricky.

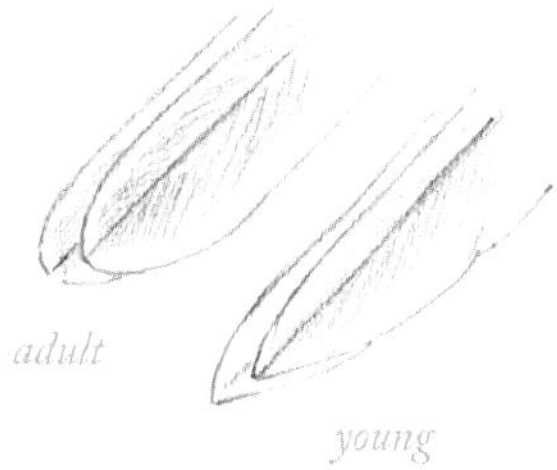

adult

young

shape of tail feathers of adult and young Greenfinches

From a general point of view, older males are more full-coloured, that is to say greener and yellower overall, particularly on the face and on the breast. The same applies to females, older individuals of which have a large and distinct yellowish-green area on the belly and olive-green colours in the face, whereas young females in their first 'full-grown' plumage have no or only extremely little green in the plumage and are mostly brownish and greyish.

In literature, the male's colour is usually described as brownish-green on the mantle, which tends to tally with many younger males and some older ones in winter. Many old males however, seem to work with two ground colours, a deep yellowish-green colour and a quite neutral ash-grey tone which is noticeable mainly on the ear-coverts and on the flanks. The primarily green feathers have also, in fresh plumage, a grey fringe at the extreme edges. When the green and grey shades are mixed, a soft olive-grey colour is created which often appears 'turned off' and camouflages the bird in the vegetation. The colour of the mantle feathers can tend towards grey or towards brown and at one time I imagined that there were two different types, a grey-green and a brown-green morph. But I believe rather that they exhibit a sliding colour scale. With the males whose grey shades are neutral, in other words have no brown tinges, a wonderful meeting between green and neutral grey is formed. Old males often have a relatively sharp golden-green colour on the forehead and on the throat. When the grey fringes disappear towards the beginning of spring the green colour is switched on, it becomes more golden and the bird can look purely exotic.

Grey females

The females, the real nymphs, are known less as Chloris and more as the winter standards' goddess. They are grey, grey-brown and grey-green and, in their colour range, impossible to distinguish from the agricultural fields' autumn plant population. There is still some green behind the drab colours on the older females, but we must sharpen the eye's cones during late autumn for them to be visible. The outermost edges of the primaries however, even on the most discreetly coloured female, create a yellow 'opening' towards the spring and the sun. Older females are normally almost unstreaked and vary from having a cooler green-grey tone to being predominantly brown, not uncommonly with a faint

Naples yellow shade over the throat and the belly.

Young females not unusually, lack yellow or green on the body except on the rump and on the primaries. They have shades of grey-buff and brown and present no hints of green at all. Other young females have a greenish-yellow colour on the belly. Females in their first winter are not uncommonly clearly streaked on the mantle and breast. The tips of the tertials and the greater coverts, if they have not been renewed, are lighter grey and on the face there appears a warm grey supercilium and a more distinct band along the cheek and they often have a paler lore. They look more aged than those females which are into their second year of life. If the tail feathers can be seen, the fact that they are pointed and worn is always the safest way of identifying a specific bird as being in its first winter plumage.

The tertials on the Greenfinch can vary a little in pattern and their appearance distinguishes between juveniles and adults. On juvenile birds the tertials are usually diffusely darker centrally and the longest one is dark also towards the outer web; typically, the outer web towards the tip contrasts with the base and is light grey or grey-buff. On old birds the darker centre is more distinctly set off, more square and restricted to the inner web; the feather tip is straighter and the entire outer web is of one and the same colour. Old males have almost uniformly neutral grey tertials with only a blackish spot or square on the inner web. Females have more dark in the centre and the ground colour can vary from grey to pure brown. Young of the year may replace one, two or all three tertials and they are then similarly patterned to those of the adults. Most often it is the innermost or the two innermost that are renewed, but sometimes only the middle one.

Birds in autumn

When the breeding season is over, towards the autumn, the Greenfinches gather in small groups which make for plant-rich edge zones of the cultivated landscape, cattle sheds, beaches and heathlands where various plants offer an abundance of seeds. Where I live on Gotland, viper's-bugloss and chicory are popular, as well as groundsel, mugwort and grass-leaved orache. When these plants' seeds have all been harvested, the Greenfinches readily visit dog-rose bushes, whitebeams or rowans. They are mainly out for the seeds and work the rose hips on the

young female
Ung hona, första vinterdräkt
ad
juv
juv
adult female

twigs. We therefore often see what look like half-eaten rose hips still left on the bushes. If you study your Greenfinches outside the window more closely, you can sometimes see remnants of rose hips and other berries which have collected in the bristles around the corners of the bill and on the lowermost forehead. Then you understand why the Greenfinch has acquired a small moustache. This prevents sticky fruit pulp from ending up in the facial feathers.

Death and regeneration

When we feed the birds, we have to weigh up our proximity to the birds against their safety. Greenfinches 'explode' from the ground when a Sparrowhawk or cat attacks and they are so fast that they usually die if they fly into a window pane. House Sparrows, Tree Sparrows and tits take shelter in the vegetation, while Greenfinches head skywards to trust in their speed. A reflection of the sky in a window pane or a view through the room's opposing windows is seen as a flight route. Some species are affected more than others and the Greenfinch is one such. We should therefore think about how we position a seed-dispenser which attracts Greenfinches. Perhaps arrange it so that the food site is at an angle to the window. I usually provide food into May in order to attract some of the passing Bramblings and Siskins which often drop in during April. In one year even a Serin *Serinus serinus* turned up in the first week of May, so it can be worth it in more ways than one. But the gain is to an equally great extent the Greenfinches, the males of which are, from March, more territorial and often unfold the yellow carpals, raise the tail and sing with great intensity. The song consists of long trills which constantly change in tone and speed, mixed with long indrawn '*tziiiyoh*' notes which are sometimes rather hoarse in tone. The species calls with a varied '*dvueet*', which is also interwoven into the song. In flight the Greenfinch gives a bouncing or rolling 'joop-oop-oop-oop'. The Greenfinches' recital can sometimes be deafening when I am filling the seed-dispenser in the middle of the wood anemone season. One often sees males feeding females and the associations with spring regeneration come even more to mind.

female
2014
male

GOLDFINCH

Carduelis carduelis

THE GOLDFINCH's Swedish name, *steglits*, is onomatopoeic and one of the most accurate. Despite its distinctive appearance, this species is more often noticed from its call, '*stickelitt*', especially in summer when trees and bushes are covered with leaves. At Vamlingbo church and rectory in south Gotland, where I have exhibitions of work, their calls are heard all the time in summer and they seem to have ideal conditions there. The churchyard is enclosed by rows of lime trees, an avenue of maples leads down to the rectory and, in the park, stand solitary ash trees and small-leaved elms overgrown with ivy. All around there is open agricultural land and meadows which are grazed by sheep and a few Ardennes carthorses. The nearest farmyard also has a gravel pit and a haulage company with large areas of ground where the winter's ploughs stand, full of all manner of weeds. In late summer when Goldfinches, Greenfinches and Linnets have young and there is constant chirping and twittering in the old elmwoods, it is always the Goldfinches' spirited calls that cut through the chorus.

If we look at the Goldfinch's occurrence as a breeding bird in Sweden, we get a clear picture of the areas where humans have lived and cultivated the land for a long time and the fact that the species avoids wooded regions. It is common in a belt from Uppland down across the Lake Malar region to Västergötland, also in Scania and Halland and on Gotland and Öland and nearby coastal regions in east Småland. It has a preference for field edges, pasture fields and abandoned or disturbed areas with numbers of thistles and burdocks: it is there that one has the best chance of seeing it from late summer and during the autumn and winter. During the breeding season Goldfinches often live in larger gardens, in parks and around clumps of trees in arable country. The number of breeding pairs in Sweden is estimated at 16,000. The species is much rarer north of the Dal River (Dalälven), but occurs occasionally and locally along the Norrland coast

well up into the Gulf of Bothnia. Many birds leave the country in October, but how large a proportion of the population overwinters we do not know. The number varies also between different years depending on food supply. In winters with much snow it is harder to find food, since fewer seed-bearing winter standards are accessible. We see Goldfinches most commonly during the autumn, when these richly coloured finches move among different thistle stands in the cultivated landscape.

Thistle specialist

burdock

With its long and very pointed bill the Goldfinch is a specialist on seeds of composite plants such as spear thistle, teasel, groundsel and greater knapweed. The red 'face' consists of quite short, stiff feathers and may be an adaptation to withstand wear when the bird sinks it bill deep inside the seedheads. The Goldfinch has short legs and powerful feet and is skilled in climbing winter standards. It frequently perches and holds the inflorescence while working it. The flocks often appear restless and move from one clump to another, but sometimes smaller groups will stay for longer, quite silent and attack a group of burdocks. They often move around within relatively large areas but obviously have to check where suitable food is growing; they regularly return to the same spot but rarely behave like Greenfinches, which can live in a limited area for a long time. At the farm community where I live in southwest Gotland I know that, if there are burdocks present, sooner or later the Goldfinches will come there during the autumn. They eat items from the ground too, and regularly take seeds from trees such as birch, alder and pine. During the breeding season, which lasts from May to August and involves a couple or perhaps sometimes three broods, the young are fed also with insects. They often nest in small loose colonies and towards late summer small family parties can be seen searching for food together.

It is only in recent years that Goldfinches have started to come to birdtables. There is no clear answer to the question of what made them change their behaviour, but one of the reasons may be that they had very recently increased in numbers and with that perhaps more also overwinter. A few snowy winters, following a long period of mild winters with little snow during the first decade of the twenty-first century, may have contributed.

Dazzling colours

The Goldfinch is unmistakable owing to its richly coloured and contrasty pattern. In the late-summer and autumn flocks however, we often see birds with a juvenile head which can cause some surprise. These lack the adults' distinctive head pattern, which is instead pale buffish with dark markings, looking like small dots; however they do have the species' characteristic wing and tail patterns. The males are normally somewhat bigger than the females and have a longer bill and the red extends farther behind the eye. The red forehead varies somewhat in tone and sometimes birds with an orange-red facial pattern are seen, these presumably being younger birds. The beautiful ochre colour on the breast is concentrated in two large patches on the breast sides and continues down on to the flanks. It also forms a narrow breastband. The strong contrast between the black wing and the bright yellow patches is the Goldfinch's most prominent distinguishing mark, the character which first catches the eye of the observer. When at times it balances itself and spreads its tail, it reveals a lovely panel of white on the outer tail feathers. In flight the red patch on the face often looks simply dark, but it gleams again when the birds drop down into a group of thistles. The Goldfinch has nicely shaped buffish-white patches at the tips of the black tertials and tail feathers. In fully fresh plumage they have a small border of ochre on the uppertail-coverts.

adult male
female
young male

SISKIN
Carduelis spinus

FOR US ORNITHOLOGISTS, THE SISKIN gives itself away mainly by its fast 'rippling' flight call alternating with characteristic '*tsiu*' notes or a more drawn-out '*tsiiluu*'. The call is inflected in an obvious way and has a sharp, almost slightly creaking tone. In the forest it is often not altogether easy to see well, as it moves high up in the tops of the spruces or simply flies over in deep undulations. Its silhouette reveals that it is a small finch and that it has a shorter tail in comparison with that of the Common Redpoll. The flight is fast and bounding and in autumn and winter the birds usually travel in flocks in search of the region's alder trees. If you have Siskins at your birdtable or happen to come across a group searching for seeds on the ground, they are often not shy and will allow themselves to be watched at close range. The male is generally green, yellow and black and contrastingly marked, with a black forehead and a lovely yellow over the rest of the head and the breast. The wing has a characteristic pattern which immediately distinguishes them from Greenfinches. The females are more moderately coloured, more grey and clearly streaked and the yellowish areas anteriorly are more pale greenish-yellow, like not quite ripe lemons.

The finches' precision mechanic

If the Greenfinch can be said to be the finches' unskilled labourer, then the Siskin is the precision mechanic whose bill is a precision tool for picking seeds out of cones, especially those of spruce and alder. Siskins can turn up in one part of the country in one year but be virtually gone in the following year. Spruce cones are abundant in some years but can then be lacking during subsequent years, so the Siskin appears locally in greatly varying numbers. Spruce cones take three years to develop; they start to open and release their seeds in late winter and this continues during the spring when the Siskins begin to nest. The alder too, retains its seeds until well into late winter. However, the Siskins can profit from their cones as early as autumn and during winter. They also consume pine seeds and a number of other plant seeds. Most Siskins migrate in autumn southwest to central and west Europe. The supply of seed-bearing alder cones influences the number overwintering in Sweden.

If, like me, you feed birds also in April, you will probably have noticed the spring passage of Siskins. One April day, with winds from the southwest, you suddenly get a visit from quite a small group even though they were conspicuous by their absence during the winter. During the autumn passage I never see any Siskins at the seed-dispensers, in part owing to the fact that I feed less regularly, but probably because there is then enough food out in the woods and fields. While the Greenfinches usually work in lower plant vegetation and bushes, the Siskins are most often up in the trees and are thus not so easy to observe when foraging. They are seen most easily in autumn in alder trees. Siskins are much smaller than Greenfinches and they move acrobatically in the branches, hanging and climbing in all directions with their short but strong legs and feet. There are 820,000 pairs breeding in Sweden, where they are found across the whole country except in the mountains north of the coniferous-forest limit. The really important areas are older and middle-aged spruce forest, so the numbers are naturally fewer in the larger agricultural plains. Generally speaking, the species has been favoured by the extensive planting of spruce which took place during the previous century.

Singing Siskins

The Siskins are genial acquaintances and they are energetic and vivacious. They readily take nuts or peanuts, as well as smaller seeds and spillage from sunflower seeds. Like Greenfinches, they often sing when perched in the trees round about. The Siskin has a fast and lively song, a clear twittering with various elements of harsh rippling notes and mimicry; now and then there is usually a long, somewhat unexpected wheezing '*drieeeeeh*', as if it has touched down and is braking with its sharp claws on a glass surface. If there are several singing, it becomes a striking

old male

pine seeds

chorus. When the male sings above the breeding territory he performs, like the Greenfinch, a flight song in which his yellow wingbars are conspicuous in the morning sun.

Distinguishing between immatures and adults

The juveniles moult during the summer and autumn and then become more like the older birds. Depending on which brood they were from and therefore how early they fledged, this moult takes place over a lengthy period of the summer and autumn and one can therefore see birds still moulting into October. Normally all body feathers and most of the lesser and median secondary coverts are replaced. They change also, to a varying extent, the greater coverts, tertials and odd tail feathers. As usual, it is the appearance of these feathers that you should examine if you wish to know if a bird is in its first winter or is an older one. What you should look for is whether there is a visible difference between new adult feathers and old juvenile ones.

We often see on males a distinction between the new coverts, which are blacker and have a broad green or greenish-yellow tip and the inner juvenile ones, which are lighter and more brown and have a narrower and often yellowish-white outer edge. Some have changed only one feather, whereas most have replaced six or eight and it can then be harder to see the outer juvenile ones. Sometimes they change one, two or all three tertials and there the difference between old and new can be easier to detect, especially on immatures which have changed almost all greater secondary coverts. The new ones then have an obviously broader and more complete, pale outer edging on the outer half of the feather. New or adult tertials often give a two-tone impression, with the inner part green or greenish-grey and the outer part whitish. The juvenile tertials are more uniformly light yellow-buff, narrower and often more worn.

On older males, the yellow patch at the base of the primaries is generally longer, more extended and considerably brighter yellow in colour. Many young males in autumn do not have so pronounced a black crown, as it is partially concealed by paler grey fringes and can besides be broken up by remaining juvenile feathers. Males have a small black patch beneath the bill which in winter is concealed by greyish-white fringes but which is conspicuous during the spring. In autumn there is often a greyish haze over the males' colour tones which is created by pale grey tips or fringes.

The difference in colour between old and new feathers applies also to females, but I think that it is often more difficult to determine moult limits on females. With young females however, the moult seems often to include fewer greater secondary coverts. The new ones are darker, blacker, and have a broader yellow or yellowish-white tip. In spring these differences remain, but the retained juvenile tertials can be very worn and more faded and brown. Bearing in mind the species' nomadic existence, the place where they have been living can to a great degree influence how worn they may come to be when they appear again in Scandinavia. Generally, older females have more yellow extending down over the breast and narrower streaking. Furthermore, the pale border over the eyebrow and down around the ear-coverts is more often more bright yellow and less streaked on older females. Also valid for females is that the contrast between new and older tertials and greater secondary coverts is the character which most reliably separates young and old individuals.

But one really should not analyse the age of these charming little finches, as it is perfectly fine simply to delight in their cute expressions and sink into the male's beautiful gaudy display of colours. With their pointed awl and black peaked cap they are on the way to the whistling tops of the nordic spruce forests.... if there are any cones, otherwise they continue eastwards towards Russia and perhaps these very individuals will never pass by your part of the country again.

young female

female winter
male winter

LINNET

Carduelis cannabina

THE LINNET is somewhat bigger than a Common Redpoll but smaller than a Greenfinch. After it has assumed its winter plumage in August–September it becomes fairly anonymous, grey-buff and generally brown-streaked. The bright white outer webs on the primary and tail feathers are possibly what stand out most in this plumage. The crimson-red colour on the forehead and breast which the male has during the breeding season appears gradually as a result of fringe loss during the spring and early summer. The females are dull grey-buff with distinct dark streaking, while the males have a warmer ochre ground colour with rust-brown tones over the wings. In the autumn flocks however, all the birds look similar at first sight.

In the latter part of September and in October the Linnet migrates south. In mild autumns occasional flocks or individuals remain behind in southernmost Sweden, usually in regions near the coast and they may attempt to overwinter. This happens regularly only in Scania and Halland. The Linnet is very uncommon at winter feeding sites, but despite this it has got on to the list of sixty or so species which visit birdtables. It arrives from the latter part of March in south Scandinavia, but more generally during April.

The Linnet is associated with agricultural country and thrives in bushy terrain with dry ground and pasturelands. In autumn and winter it often gathers in dense flocks on stubble fields and wasteland. Its bill is stout and always darker than that of the Twite. The white outer webs on the primaries are obvious right out to the tips, whereas those on the Twite are more marked on the inner part. The Linnet gives a dry bouncing '*tett-ett-ett*' in flight. It sings year round, in winter quietly and conversationally with twittering and rolling notes.

TWITE

Carduelis flavirostris

THE TWITE is in many ways more like a large, streaked, Common Redpoll or Lesser Redpoll than a Linnet. It looks generally saturated warm brown and with a curry-yellow tone of varying extent over the face and chin. The bill is yellowish with a small dark tip. The pale wingbar across the greater secondary coverts is very prominent in the field. The inner primaries have a broad white outer web, something which is very apparent in flight. The rump is of a nice dark pink colour, which is difficult to see in the field but can be perceived just as the birds alight on the ground. Compared with the Linnet, Twites often look a little bushy or well insulated and Common Redpoll-like in plumage. When the flock takes wing, Linnet-like '*tett*' calls are heard, but also a call characteristic of the species, a slightly drawn-out nasal sibilant '*tveeihtt*'. Linnets and Common Redpolls are often somewhat restless and easily take flight and the call is therefore a good way of detecting Twites. The species is not a regular visitor to birdtables, but occasional individuals may join redpolls and turn up at feeding sites.

The distribution in Scandinavia is mainly tied to Norway, where Twites breed commonly in open heath-like terrain with low vegetation, both in coastal regions and on upland moors. During migration and as overwinterers they are usually found on short-grazed coastal meadows and various wastelands such as in harbour and dock areas and at refuse dumps. The species' Swedish name, *vinterhämpling*, means 'winter linnet', taken from the fact that Twites arrive in south Sweden in late autumn, the peak passage usually occurring at the end of October and the beginning of November, about the same time as Common Redpolls are moving southwards. The direction of the passage is often southerly or southeasterly and they are met with sparsely over the whole of south and central Sweden. The species is however, more numerous in west Sweden and in Denmark, where large flocks are seen on passage and in winter.

COMMON REDPOLL

Carduelis flammea

FOR ME AND MANY OF MY GENERATION THE COMMON REDPOLL is seen as very much a bird of the north, a nomad which in some years turns up in large flocks in late autumn when the cold sets in in the north. It can appear in large numbers in some years, while in the following year there are few. In summer, the species' display flight in wide arcs above the upland birch forest is a characteristic feature for anybody walking in the mountains. Here the form involved is the northern race *flammea*, the one first described by Linnaeus. The fact that it is grey, brown and white and fluffy like a reindeer-skin rug, reinforces the feeling that it is a bird from northern regions. This picture has in recent years been challenged by the entry into Sweden of the Lesser Redpoll. This smaller race *cabaret*, has since several decades back become an established breeding bird in mainly southwest Sweden but also locally right up to south Norrland.

The northern Common Redpolls are most often encountered in restless, tight flocks which drop down into a birch or into a stand of orache or mugwort. On the birdtable lists for 'Winter birds on our doorstep', the species moves on a switchback course between tenth and thirtieth place. My own experience is that they seldom remain through the winter, but that they turn up occasionally only then to disappear again. I usually see just one or two birds, which seem to have come a little out of their way or have accompanied Siskins in April; however, groups of up to fifty individuals are not uncommon at the birdtable in other parts of Sweden. The estimated Swedish population is just under half a million pairs.

The nomad

The northern Common Redpoll's life revolves, to a large degree, around the birch tree in the same way as the Siskin's does around the spruce.

The birch blooms when the trees are leafing, ripens during the summer and drops its seeds towards late summer and autumn. Birch seeds which thaw out from the snow then become an important food surce when the redpolls arrive back in the north. During the breeding season it is, in addition to birch seeds, also the occurrence of the autumnal moth (*Epirrita autumnata*) that influences numbers. The supply of autumnal moth larvae goes in cycles: in years with plenty of these caterpillars in a region the Common Redpolls nest in large numbers. In other years they may be less numerous. In certain years when the seed set of spruce is very good, the redpolls may stop in the coniferous belt on spring migration and raise a first brood of young and then continue up to the upland birch forest for a second brood. There is something of the nomad in its behaviour, as it follows the food supply and can in some years be numerous on passage and as an overwinterer in middle and southern Sweden, while in other years few individuals are seen. The birds often migrate relatively late in the year, from the latter part of October and into November, but they move around through the winter depending on food supply. The direction of migration is more southerly or southeasterly, while most other finches move southwestwards in the autumn. Redpolls are not faithful to the place where they were reared.

Red patch on the forehead

A flock of Common Redpolls is always fascinating to watch. They have a fluffy plumage, an 'arctic fur coat' and a long tail with which they balance when creeping around in a birch tree or a clump of winter standards. Just as with many other species which occur in flocks, they all look similar at first. But if you look more closely, you see several differences among individuals.

In autumn and winter, Common Redpolls are often rather warm-coloured with elements of yellowish-grey and brown. All have the characteristic crimson-red patch on the forehead, but it can vary in size and brightness. It is only the adult males that have a pinkish breast and a rosy colour on the face, as if they had eaten berries when not wearing a bib. While they lay two clutches, it is a minority in the autumn flocks, perhaps one in ten, that have a pink breast, in other words that are adult

Common Redpoll, female

Lesser Redpoll, female

males. Gradually during the late winter and spring the pale warm-coloured fringes fade and are worn off and the birds become more and more grey-toned and brown-grey on the back. If you are visited by northern Common Redpolls in April, they appear predominantly colourless except for the red forehead and, on males, breast. This colourless grey impression is strengthened during the spring, for when they are encountered in the upland birch forest in early summer they seem for the most part grey-streaked with a red forehead.

Lesser Redpoll

Lesser Redpolls are a race of the Common Redpoll, *cabaret*, which historically bred in only two regions in Europe, one in north England and Scotland and the other in conifer forest in the Alps. They are sometimes treated as a separate, full species. The English birds bred originally in bushy country or low-grown woodland, often with birch, or in pine plantations. Lesser Redpolls expanded their range in a first wave in the 1800s, when they spread southwards in England and reached the Continent. A second wave during the 1900s reached southwestern Scandinavia and in Sweden Lesser Redpolls arrived in the 1970s and became established on the west coast. A major cause of the general expansion is considered to be an increase in new planting of conifer forest which in the growth phase created perfect habitats of dense young forest. In recent years the Lesser Redpoll has begun to nest also along the Baltic coast. The diet is like of the northern birds, with seeds from birch an important food source.

Lesser Redpolls frequently turn up at birdtables and typically this often involves one or two birds. Usually we see instinctively that it is a Lesser Redpoll simply through the fact that the colour is more saturated brown and buff and that it is smaller than a Common Redpoll. In particular, the cheek and the breast side usually have a saturated yellow-brown colour, like the wingbar, which stands out from that of 'normal' Common Redpolls. Their appearance can bring to mind the Twite, especially if the red forehead is not seen. It is conceivable that Lesser Redpolls and Common Redpolls will interbreed in some years and that birds with a more intermediate appearance may turn up.

Bouncing and metallic whirring

The flight call is a bouncing '*jitt*' and '*jiji-jitt*', often in combination and repeated in quick succession. The advertising call is a more drawn-out slightly dissonant '*chueet*' or '*chuiiht*', not wholly unlike the Siskin's. The song, which it delivers while flying in wide arcs, is the flight call mixed with varying very fast trills or cicada-like series of notes and drawn-out metallic whirring series. The flight and advertising calls resemble the Siskin's but are, as already mentioned, more bouncing and have a special metallic dissonance. The Siskin's flight call is more 'rippling' and vowel-less and its long advertising call more pure in tone.

ARCTIC REDPOLL

Carduelis hornemanni

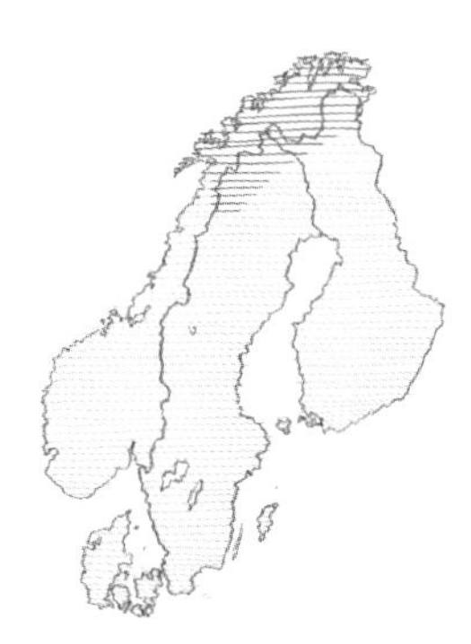

THE ARCTIC REDPOLL normally occurs in the high-arctic treeless terrain and is usually treated as a full species. Genetically it is inseparable from the Common Redpoll and is, in appearance, very like the latter, and hybrids also possibly occur. In some years Arctic Redpolls may breed in the birch zone, but normally they are found in the willow region of the mountains and on coastal tundra. In winter they remain for the most part in the north, but occasional individuals accompany the Common Redpolls southwards in late autumn. They also return to the breeding sites earlier than the Common Redpoll does.

If one sees an Arctic Redpoll on the tundra, pale and washed out as if seen through a steamy glass window pane and with just a pale rosy-coloured breast, it is simple to identify the species. But when, farther south, one examines a flock of northern Common Redpolls to see if there is an Arctic Redpoll among them, one often ends up puzzled; some Arctic Redpoll individuals look typical, others seem to be intermediate between the two.

The main criterion for the species is an unstreaked white area on the lower back and over the rump and no shaft streaks, or only thin ones, on the undertail-coverts. The streaking on the underside is more restricted and often consists of a few 'over-exposed' streaks on the flanks at the rear. Older males often look obviously pale, dusted with white and with a weak rosy tint on the breast. Birds in their first winter are more Common Redpoll-like but usually paler overall, with a golden-ochre tinge anteriorly and a slightly warmer red or orange-red forehead patch. They normally have a band across the lower back which is unstreaked white or faintly warm-toned. Occasional young females have a hint of streaks or spots on the back. We often see Arctic Redpolls as looking slightly more elongated with a longer tail and shorter bill, the latter even more enclosed in bristles.

immature
adult male

PINE GROSBEAK

Pinicola enucleator

IF I ATTEMPTED earlier to describe the difference in status or ranking for the Chaffinch and Brambling, then the Pine Grosbeak is in a class of its own. If we say that there is Pine Grosbeak in hand, that means that they seem to be on the move southwards, so we ornithologists get something 'religious' in sight. The Pine Grosbeak is in some way the king of the finches irrespective of how cheeky the Hawfinch looks. The reason is not only its size and fantastic coloration but also the fact that, for us in south Sweden, it is difficult to see and symbolises the very essence of the taiga. Just as with the Bullfinch, it is hard to make up one's mind whether it is the female or the male that is the most handsome. The Pine Grosbeak is circumpolar in distribution, in other words it breeds right around the entire northern hemisphere, in the northernmost part of the coniferous belt. The Swedish population is estimated at 10,000 pairs and it nests in older spruce forest with a deciduous element, mainly birch and rowan, and a rich understorey of berry-bearing scrub.

They are like trolls, slightly too big, jovial, with grey underclothes of wadmal. In preparation for the visit to the community, they have put on best clothes that are much too skin-tight, the male in wine-red, the female in golden-green. Grey is visible through the slits and the seams but they wear their clothes with pride. All the wing feathers are hemmed at the edges with what looks like silver thread or greyish-white silk thread, a piece of embroidery for kings. The large bill and the quietly gazing eyes do make the bird seem like a little troll that has ended up outside its mossy spruce forest, sitting in a snow-covered rowan in the city market-place, greedily feeding.

Females and first-winter males are very similar and probably cannot be told apart. Both have a grey base colour and a variable golden-green to bitter-orange-coloured tone on the head, breast, mantle and rump. The extent of the colour varies among individuals and on some it is

young male
adult female

present only on the head and breast. The colour is hard to define; it has the same effect as flowering haircap moss, as it sometimes seems golden-green but in some cases pale orange. Birds which are greenish can have some bitter-orange-coloured feathers on the head. It looks as if they have grown in in different periods and the colour pigmentation has been influenced by different food intakes. Older females can possibly be recognised by the fact that they have a golden-green shade on the webs of the primaries, just as the adult wine-red males have a weak rosy shade. On young birds the pale outer webs appear narrower and they look simply whitish.

The silly fool

According to several authors, the Pine Grosbeak was in the past called the 'silly fool' by bird-catchers in Sweden. Magnus von Wright states in 1859 that the bird has acquired this less than flattering name 'owing to the fact that during the satisfying of his voracious appetite he does not notice or pay attention to the danger which threatens him in the same tree (often small rowan) on the berries of which he is gorging himself, but allows himself to be dragged down by somebody at the end of a longish stick, a fishing-rod or suchlike fixed snare'. Since the bird was obviously well known in common speech during the 1800s, we may suppose that it also was more regular as a visitor in winter in south and central Sweden. According to Sven Nilsson's *Skandinavisk fauna* from 1859, it was more uncommon at that time compared with forty to fifty years earlier. Maybe the Pine Grosbeak bred farther south and in greater numbers during the centuries before Nilsson's book, when the climate was considerably cooler than it is today and there was probably more older spruce forest with luxuriant undergrowth of berry shrubs in large parts of Norrland.

The rowanberrys' seeds

As a visitor to birdtables it is usually in Norrbotten that the species turns up with some regularity. Since they are attracted to rowans they are often found in towns and villages, where they are quite fearless and we could see this food supply as a kind of birdtable. It is in fact not the fruit pulp itself that they eat but only the seeds. The bird's specific eithet *enucleator* comes from the Latin *enucleare*, which indeed means 'to release from the core' or 'to remove the pips'. You can tell them, if by nothing else, by the fact that they often have lots of fruit pulp around the bill and that they take their time to work a berry, just as readily taking shrivelled and blackening berries as they do red and fresh ones.

During a stroll when thoughts of this came to mind, I tried to find out myself how difficult it could be to extract rowan seeds from a rowanberry. I picked some and began to grind one up in my mouth. In the first attempt I got one seed out, but was unsure how many seeds there should be in each berry. On a subsequent occasion I set about the task more systematically and dissected a number of rowanberries with my sharpest spectacles and a fine knife. The result was four seeds, each four millimetres long, like garlic cloves in shape but flatter. We see the Pine Grosbeaks perch jovially and, as it appears, 'chew' on the fruit pulp for a while until the berry is completely without pips. There were not always however, four seeds in each berry; perhaps not all seeds had developed or maybe some other smaller organism also ate rowanberry seeds. In my imagination I thought of how this organism interpreted the Pine Grosbeak's treatment of its secure and secluded rowanberry home, as some kind of voracious giant troll.

Since the rowanberry seeds are dispersed by thrushes and Waxwings by passing through the intestine undigested, I assume that the Pine Grosbeak crushes them in the bill first. The Pine Grosbeak is a hardy bird which also eats buds and shoots of trees and various seeds and pips. During the breeding season it consumes some insects too. It does well in the darkness and the cold which prevails in its home districts in the winter time.

Visit to Gotland

In years when many Pine Grosbeaks are observed in the south in Sweden, many of the birds doubtless come from the east. They seem to dislike travelling over open sea and this is a true rarity on Gotland. Only once have I seen them on my home island. I was on the way to collect one of the children from the ferry at Visby one day before Christmas and had heard that a small group of Pine Grosbeaks had turned up around a stand of larch trees. An opportunity I could not miss. I got there and made my way up a steep hill from where I could overlook the larch trees where they would be. It was snowing quite heavily and I stood for almost an hour and watched. Time and time again I allowed myself to be fooled by first one and then another Greenfinch which occasionally turned up. I saw the ferry coming in to the harbour and time began to get short. Then I heard their characteristic call, a bubbling flute-like '*juliliu*', and gazed out into the snow-laden air. They came flying along, heavy and long-tailed, in deep undulations, five individuals which circled around a couple of times before dropping down into one of the larches.

The Pine Grosbeak also has a fast double-call, '*julli-julli*', or an even faster '*lillill*', almost like a Quail call. The birds sing also in winter, and especially with subsong. They then perch and chatter quietly somewhat like Bullfinches, with advertising calls, short fluted calls and trills. The song has a certain similarity to thrush song, as that of some Redwings, a fast drawn-out twittering series with deep fluting sounds, surprisingly fast and elegant to be coming from a forest troll.

Other red winter finches

In Sweden we have three species of crossbill whose appearance can recall that of the Pine Grosbeak, the males red and the females green. Crossbills have specialised on seeds from conifer cones and adjust the breeding season according to the seed set of the various coniferous trees. The Common Crossbill *Loxia curvirostra* prefers spruce cones, the Parrot Crossbill *L. pytyopsittacus* pine cones and the Two-barred Crossbill *L. leucoptera* cones of larch trees. In fact, crossbills, and especially Two-barred Crossbills, readily eat seeds from rowanberry trees and so they sometimes appear in towns and villages in the same way as Pine Grosbeaks do. Sometimes crossbills are noted even at birdtables, but this is exceptional. Parrot and Common Crossbills often nest in February, since the spruce and pine cones have ripened and are waiting to release their seeds just before the spring growing season. Closest in colour to the Pine Grosbeak male is the Two-barred Crossbill, which has a cold cerise colour tone; however, it is smaller and has white wingbars.

BULLFINCH

Pyrrhula pyrrhula

WHEN I WENT TO nursery school, everyone had to paint a wooden candlestick which we would take home for Advent Sunday, or that was the idea. I came home with half-a-dozen medium-grey candlesticks decorated with a winter bush occupied by red-bellied Bullfinches. My mother loved Bullfinches, a reminder of her childhood winters in Jämtland. Bullfinches are thought always to have been the symbol of Christmas, perhaps not so surprising in view of the warm red belly and matching grey mantle. It appears quite simply created as a Christmas decoration. Usually however, it is just when the cold weather sets in and the snow is settling deep in the forest that it comes out to the food we have provided. The Bullfinch comes about fifth among the bird species seen most on the 'Winter birds on our doorstep' list and often makes first place in Jämtland. It likes spruce forest and the highest densities are found in Norrland and in the south Swedish highlands. In Sweden there are about 380,000 breeding pairs. At the birdtable it has a preference for hemp seed, but it can live throughout the winter on buds from deciduous trees and even spruce. Bullfinches seem to have a certain weakness for fruit-tree buds.

The red colour

There is something magical in the Bullfinch's red colour. I have never managed to understand if it is the character of the whole bird, the contrast with the white, grey and black, or some inherent quality in the colour and the matter that gives it its fantastic beauty. Sometimes it seems to be bright pale red, glossy like a silk ribbon, at other times exquisitely toned down and soft in a way that makes me want to hold the bird, or rather to paint the way the light creates volume across the belly. If, as seldom happens, one catches sight of a male singing early one April morning, his breast is bright warm red. But on raw winter days with a grey sky and white snow this colour is at its most beautiful, like a magic charm without comparison. Presumably it is just the wavelength in the red light that switches something on in us and the black and grey become a kind of sober framework. When the male ruffles up his plumage the underparts acquire a certain cold red, or towards the belly a rosy tone, then he blossoms at his most intense. In the book *Dagrar* ('Light and shade') I wrote that Bullfinches without snow are like a brownie in a tracksuit: it is somehow not real. I often see Bullfinches on migration in April. They frequently look for seeds on some ground beneath old deciduous trees and the red colour clashes with the red-brown leaves.

The sober female

Every time I look at Bullfinches I wrestle with myself over whether it is the male or the female that is the more attractive. The male is the obvious choice but, the more I look at them, the more I incline towards the female's sober plumage. She varies, too. The pastel-like buff-brown colour of the belly reminds me of a colour chart for warm brown lipstick or eye shadow, or perhaps it is rouge I am thinking of? On the cheeks it is warmer, more bright brownish-pink, towards the belly sides more grey and subdued. The sober colour comes from the fact that the mantle is brown, but colder and darker brown and sets off the soft colour transitions of the underparts. The neck-boa is grey but otherwise as the male's and the crown and wings are black with a blue gloss. The outer web of the outer three primaries has a nice sulphur-yellow to whitish-grey colour which, when one is close enough, is surprising in its elegance.

The broad wingbar which is created by the pale tips of the greater secondary coverts is not pure white as often depicted. In any case not during the winter. The juveniles have a fresh ochre shade in the wingbar, but during the autumn moult these coverts are replaced from the inner ones outwards by broader-edged grey ones. Through the winter therefore, one can distinguish most young birds when one sees the grey wingbar ending with a paler warm-toned area towards the lower edge of the wing. It sometimes requires that you study them for a longish time, but after a while you usually see clearly which birds were hatched during the previous summer.

adult male
adult female

A peculiarity which Bullfinches share with extremely few passerines is that the black feathers have a deep Paris-blue gloss. This is most obvious on the long rounded uppertail-coverts. They have a strange velvet-like surface, a crow-like blackness and gloss which is set against the white cotton-wool of the rump. When, in the right light, you notice this you will be somewhat surprised, uplifted, fascinated, as if the red breast were not enough.

Right light

After a few windy cool days but with a blue sky, that day arrived when the sun seems never to rise. Northeast wind and soon enough the snow starts to fall, or rather to come rushing in from the sea, which is dull grey-green from slushy ice and lack of light. Then the female's colour on a bitter January day, with no snow on the ground but snowy weather approaching, can suddenly appear as greyish-mauve rather than grey-brown. Another individual may, when a weak sun penetrates through a white snowy sky, suddenly acquire a lovely yellowish-pink shade just beneath the eye. Sometimes I can only gaze and sink into these colours and on almost every occasion get something of an 'Aha!' moment. Of course, that's it, the softness and the colour in harmony with a particular branch or the leaves on the ground; well, it must be painted. My detailed depictions then appear painfully chiselled out from a box of basic colours. All the smallest nuances, the material which I think I am conjuring up with the brush, seem insensitive. The only thing is to begin again in order to feel once more the closeness to some other individual, in a different light, right here and now.

Feelings of spring

Towards late winter we often see the males approaching the females. He hops sideways closer to her and has then stretched out his body and fluffed up the belly feathers so that the wingbar is concealed. She often moves away, but when she understands what it is all about the two may perch side by side and twist and turn the tail. They may then sometimes poke each other repeatedly with the bill, as if they were kissing.

Scarlet Lake + Zink White
Scarlet Lake
P. Alizarin Crimson
Alizarin Cr.
Gouache
Cadmium Red
G. Cadmium + Zink White
Alizarin + Cadmium yellow
Scarlet + Cadmium yellow

adult male

Bullfinches are hardly known for their song. They usually take to the woods or in any event become more anonymous in April, when all spring birds suddenly fill the wood with their song. But Bullfinches not so uncommonly perch and quietly sing beside a feeding station. The song is a soft chatter with thin whistles and somewhat stifled squeaky series of notes. What many people recognise and associate with the species is its soft whistled call, '*juh*' or '*jiuh*'. Often two different notes are heard and I wonder at times if it is the same individual or a pair of birds that are whistling against each other.

Sometimes Bullfinches with a different pitch in the call appear in Sweden. These probably originate from more easterly regions. They have a more drawn-out whistle with a trumpeting tone, like a toy trumpet, quite unlike the soft whistle which we are used to. Bullfinches breed in a broad band right through Eurasia all the way to Japan. In the extreme east the male has only the cheek red, or rosy-coloured, the belly and breast being grey. It is hard to imagine a Bullfinch male without its red breast.

HAWFINCH

Coccothraustes coccothraustes

MY FIRST MEETING WITH A HAWFINCH when I was very young involved a bird which flew from beneath a beech tree one May day at Omberg, in Östergötland. I still remember the strong impression which the bird gave. The size, the weight, the white wingbands and the lovely gleaming white tail tip. It flew up at quite close range and on the ground it was completely camouflaged against the dried-out beech leaves.

The Hawfinch still has a strong foothold in Östergötland, where broadleaf woods, oak stands and gardens are a significant part of the landscape's character. The Hawfinch otherwise belongs historically to Europe's ancient deciduous woodlands, but has found itself well at home in broken cultivated country. Many trees and bushes, such as hornbeam and wild cherry, have even come to create good habitat in residential areas and parkland environments. The species spread northwards during the 1800s, when the little ice age released its grip on the Scandinavian peninsula and reached its present main distribution around the middle of the 1900s. In recent decades, with milder winters and more feeding stations, it has even expanded along the Norrland coast. On the 'Winter birds on our doorstep' list Blekinge and Scania dominate in numbers of Hawfinches noted, but the species is seen regularly, but in smaller numbers, in the whole of Svealand (the south-central part of Sweden). Numbers vary between years, but it usually comes in the top thirty.

Encounters with Hawfinches still arouse a spontaneous and strong feeling of something unique, something unusual and slightly exotic. Every time a Hawfinch makes an appearance at my birdfeeders I hear myself quietly say 'Great! Hawfinch, where are the binoculars?'. They must be looked at, be enjoyed, they cannot be simply left as if they were Tree Sparrows or Greenfinches – they demand attention.

Rough piano-mover

The body seems front-heavy because of the large head and bill. Sven Nilsson writes: 'The whole bird markedly thickset, short and stocky'. Seen as a finch it is hardly short, but it is compact and powerful, perhaps as one imagines a piano-mover. Hawfinches look rough with their black mask and gigantic bill. The bill is so big that through binoculars one can observe the material itself, the keratin's colour, variations and flashes. Its size is reinforced by the fact that it is framed in black. In winter the bill is pale fingernail-coloured, with perhaps a hint of colder shades on some parts. Nilsson describes it as 'pearl-coloured' and perhaps there is something in this, that it is pearl-grey, with a tinge of sometimes pinkish and sometimes grey-blue towards late winter. Before the coming breeding season it starts to darken, or to become blue on some parts and in April it is a gleaming grey-blue. It then becomes blacker towards early summer and during the summer often looks bicoloured, blackish-blue with a paler grey-blue base. On the ground the tail appears short and narrow, like a little rusty-buff branch stub with a paler tip. Every time the bird flies I am amazed at how much white it contains, like a fan, in the centre merging neatly into the cinnamon-coloured rump.

A major difference in plumage of the kind which many other finches present through loss of feather fringes is lacking in the Hawfinch. It is just as if it cannot be bothered to get itself a protective coloration towards autumn, but that its alertness and strength give it immunity. In actual fact the plumage is perfectly adapted to disappear against the masses of leaves on the woodland floor in a beech or oak wood. Maybe it has no need to produce edgings and broken markings as other species which live in more open terrain do. The white markings on the tail and wing are signals for danger and when one flies up all conspecifics notice this and can react at lightning speed.

Colour pattern

The male is splendid. The colours are saturated, uniform and the borders between the tones are soft and at the same time distinct. The head has a colour of its own which cannot be described as rusty-orange or rusty-buff; the tint is like rosehip soup, but the impression more like copper in direct light. It almost glistens on the forehead and deepens towards the nape, where it terminates in a neutral grey neck-boa. The breast and belly have a saturated colour, difficult to define, greyish brown-rose. The mantle is dark brown and it has a pale wingbar on the greater coverts which is rusty brown on the inside and shades into greyish-white and then cuts across to the lesser coverts, which are of the same colour. The wingbars in the spring sun can look entirely white but from the start have a faint grey-buff tinge. The rest of the wing is bluish-black with lustrous mauve and Paris-blue shades. Four of the primary tips have a remarkable ornamental shape, elongated and twisted like four small silk bow-ties lined up one after another. The secondaries have a distinct mauve lustre which at some angles of the light is dull like brushed metal, but can look very glossy at other angles.

The female is similar to the male in markings but lacks the brightness in colour, being more buff, grey and brown. It is a bit like if you reduce the saturation and the contrast in Photoshop at the same time. At a quick glance however, you can confuse the sexes. Some females look a little more colourful and can have a weak warm buff, almost rust-coloured tinge over the head. The warm brown colour is similar. A detail which separates them is that the female's secondaries are dull grey, which is visible in all lights and at all angles, as well as the fact that the outer fringe on the primaries below the silk ties also is grey. Her black mask is not so black and the lores often look more grey. In addition, she shows less white on the spread tail.

Unobtrusive nut-cracker

The Hawfinch is known in Sweden as *stenknäcken*, meaning 'the stone-cracker', from its habit of or capacity for cracking stone fruits, such as cherry stones, or sloe drupes. Its principal food it finds in broadleaf woodland where, for example, seeds from beech, hornbeam and maple are harvested from the time they ripen during the summer and further through the autumn and winter, so long as these last.

When the seeds are gone or snow covers the fallen fruits, they change over to eating buds of various broadleaf trees such as oak and elm. Often they come to birdtables at just this time and then return regu-

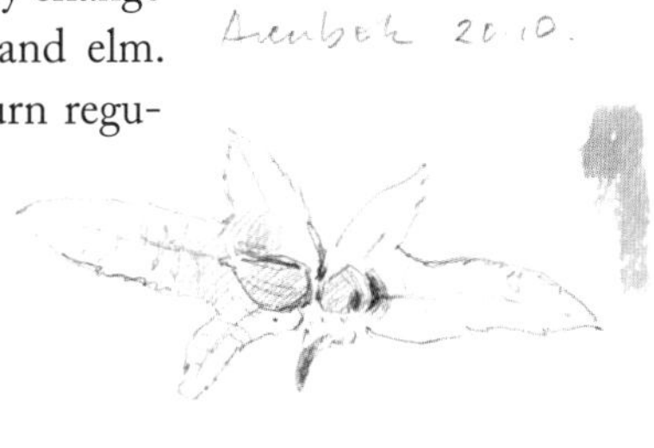

male winter

bröst
buk
rygg

bokollon

larly through the winter. Many Hawfinches however, move south in the autumn and perhaps half leave the country, others concentrating in the beech woods of Blekinge and Scania. The number at my feeding site varies annually: in some years a small group has come continuously to eat sunflower seeds, while in other years they have been absent or do not turn up until the spring passage in April.

The number in Sweden is estimated at 17,000 pairs. This can be compared with the number of Goldfinches, of which roughly the same number of pairs breed. For people who spend most of their time in Svealand or Götaland the comparison may be adequate. The Goldfinch we perceive as common and is a species which one sees with great regularity, even during the summer months but more frequently towards late summer and autumn. The Hawfinch on the other hand we see much more rarely, even in winter, away from feeding sites.

The Hawfinch is discreet and alert and it is relatively rarely that we see it spontaneously out in the forest or in gardens. If it is seen, it is usually in flight, on route between the treetops or over an open glade, or for that matter from one tree to another. The flight is fast and in deep undulations with rapid series of wingbeats alternating with glides on closed wings. Then the large white patch at the base of the primaries is prominent on the strikingly long wings.

Lacks proper song

In flight the Hawfinch often emits a sharp explosive '*tzit*', repeated at intervals of a few seconds, and sometimes also a clear ringing '*srii*'. When we watch Hawfinches at the seed-dispenser through the window, for obvious reasons we rarely hear their call. Greenfinches, Great Tits and Yellowhammers we often hear when we are replenishing food or moving about outdoors in the garden, but not Hawfinches, which fly off immediately when we approach and it takes a while before they are back. Sometimes I have sat in a hide by my seed-dispenser and then I hear the Hawfinches call. Often they seem to perch for a while in the trees round about and check that the coast is clear, and then they usually call with their sharp '*tzit*' and thereby announce that they will soon be in position. Low down at the feeding site, they usually start on the ground and search for sunflower seeds. They realise pretty quickly that it is where the Greenfinches have positioned themselves, on one of the perches alongside the plastic cylinder with sunflower seeds, that they should sit. This can lead to a few skirmishes over the most desirable perches at the dispenser and then the observer can get to see the exotic wings and tail open up. During such bickering short '*stix*' or '*stitt*' calls, dissonant and almost vowel-less, are heard. On one occasion when I was seated in the hide in April it so happened that a male had begun to sing very close by. It is a remarkable experience. With the attractive plumage pattern and the large bill one could perhaps expect something powerful, something reverberating which entices others into the oak wood, but on the contrary it feels very private, as if he were singing to himself. The song is softly chattering and pensive with the call notes, '*tzit*', pause, '*stix*', long pause, '*tzit, tsik...srii... tzik*'. What seems like an introduction to a song continues like this for a while. After a few minutes he seems to be quite self-absorbed and he tries out some more ringing vocals, little whistling or short fluting sounds, as if he was suddenly beginning to improvise. But it never becomes a proper song, as from the Greenfinch or the Linnet.

male spring

SNOW BUNTING

Plectrophenax nivalis

THE SNOW BUNTING is a high-arctic bird which breeds only above the tree-line, mostly in boulder country in high mountains, but also on coastal tundra and isands. Its distribution stretches around the whole of the northern hemisphere. In Sweden it is estimated that there are 26,000 pairs. Many birds from the Scandinavian mountain chain winter along the Norwegian coast. Snow Buntings are seen regularly in the south during passage and they winter locally in southern Sweden. During the winter months they prefer shores and open coastal regions, where various seeds constitute most of their food. They also forage on fields and stubbles.

As a visitor to the birdtable the Snow Bunting is very uncommon in winter, but it usually reaches around sixtieth place on the 'Winter birds on our doorstep' list. When the birds return to the mountains in April, it is more usual for them to visit feeding stations in valleys and villages in regions near the mountains if the weather above the tree-line is still harsh.

This is a bird which is easily identified by its size, like that of a Skylark and by the large white patches in the wings. The males in the breeding season are all white with black only on the mantle and parts of the wing and tail, while the females are less contrasty with brown-streaked mantle and usually dirty brown markings on the head. In winter plumage the dark mantle is covered by pale fringes and the head and breast have a dark brown and ochre pattern so that the whole bird appears warm in colour. Young females can be more cryptically coloured, but they always have some white on the wing and the typical 'mohican hairstyle' on the crown. Through loss of the fringes a step-by-step plumage transformation takes place during the spring. The Snow Bunting has a pleasing flight call, a fast ringing or rolling '*pirrirritt*' which is often combined with the advertising call, a slightly indrawn but desolate-sounding whistle, '*piuuh*'.

young male in winter plumage

female in winter plumage

males

YELLOWHAMMER

Emberiza citrinella

THE YELLOWHAMMER is one of the most common visitors at birdtables in at least the southern half of Sweden. It is usually among the top five most numerous species on the 'Winter birds on our doorstep' list. The great majority of the country's Yellowhammers breed in Svealand and Götaland, the south-central and the southern parts of Sweden, but it occurs also far north in the mountain valleys. The greater part of the northern breeding population moves south in October and returns in April. Solitary individuals or small flocks however, often remain behind around farms and villages, even well north if there is sufficient food. It occurs almost always in small groups or flocks during the winter.

This bunting is most common in arable country, where it forages in autumn and winter on fields and stubbles. It is a specialist on grass seeds, with its bill well adapted for that purpose. The lower mandible resembles a tiny receptable and the upper one, which is smaller, a lid or tool for stripping grass seeds from the ears. The whole structure makes me think of the head of a baleen whale, where even the slightly glossy blue-grey colour lends support to this association. The upper half is usually a little darker grey-blue. At feeding stations Yellowhammers keep low, as if pressed down against the ground and work their way forward methodically. The bill shape is poorly suited to sunflower seeds. The species does however, like corn, in contrast to finches and tits, which prefer seeds of various kinds. The classic oat sheaf with Bullfinches seen on Christmas cards of bygone days should more faithfully have shown Yellowhammers and House Sparrows.

The population of Yellowhammers in Sweden has decreased somewhat. It was one of the species which were most threatened during the 1950s and early 1960s by the mercury-impregnated sowings. The species almost disappeared from many lowland districts during that period. After mercury was banned as a means of pest-control in Sweden in 1966, the population quickly recovered. The trend has been of a slight reversal

in recent decades, even though a general stabilisation has occurred since 2000. A clear drop in the number of Yellowhammers has been noted since 2008. There is no obvious explanation for this decrease, but possibly the species has been hit by some form of sickness resembling the parasitic infection canker, which hit the Greenfinch. The number recorded for the 'Winter birds on our doorstep' survey however, has almost doubled, but this mostly reflects the increased interest in reporting what is seen around the birdtables. The species is still common in many parts of the country and the number in Sweden is estimated at 900,000 pairs.

Perhaps a Pine Bunting

The Yellowhammer is a member of the bunting group with the genus name *Emberiza*, with some ten species represented in Europe. Characteristic of these is their elongated body and long tail. Besides the Yellowhammer, Sweden has breeding populations of the Corn Bunting, Ortolan Bunting, Reed Bunting, Rustic Bunting and Little Bunting. Of these, the Yellowhammer is the only one which occurs widely at birdtables in winter. The Corn Bunting is restricted to southern Scania, where it is present all year and the Reed Bunting, a short-distance migrant, winters in small numbers in southernmost Sweden. The others are long-distance migrants. Should you see a long-tailed bunting with yellow colours and obvious streaking it is a Yellowhammer and normally it will not be confused with any other species. The Yellowhammer's appearance however, is quite variable, both individually and between the sexes and also between adult and young birds. The males, both adults and those in first-winter plumage, always have distinct yellow tones in the plumage. Many are strongly yellow-coloured, as if soaked in yellow sweet-colouring. Over this colour are drawn dark brown, olive-grey, green-grey and brick-red streaks and spots the intensity and strength of which vary.

Young males can sometimes have relatively little pure yellow, but the ground colour is present under the 'surface'. Old females and younger males can thus overlap each other in plumage. Typical is that males always have a small yellow patch on the forehead. Young females in their first winter plumage can often lack clear yellow colours but instead have a buff or greyish-buff ground colour. A flock of Yellowhammers against the snow often

young male, winter

young female, winter

looks homogeneous, light buff or yellowish with a strong dark pattern over the mantle. It is only when you have good light and can study them through binoculars that you find out how different they can appear.

In Siberia there is a closely related sister-species, the Pine Bunting *Emberiza leucocephalos*, which lacks yellow and has a general brownish-red coloration. Occasional individuals have turned up at birdtables in Sweden, but the species is a rarity. I believe that many of us have fostered a hope that a Pine Bunting will materialise out of the everyday group of yellow and striped buntings which lead a constantly dull life beneath the seed-dispenser. It has never happened to me after forty years of feeding birds in south Gotland. Periodically, in snowy winters, I have fed a hundred or so Yellowhammers and I would always go through these systematically in the hope that this Siberian rarity will turn up just for me. A number of young dull or more cold reddish-brown female Yellowhammers have over the years made my pulse race a bit, but faint yellow fringes on the primaries have always dashed all hopes, those of the Pine Bunting being white. The yellow colour has a curious way of looking white at any distance, at least through my window pane. The two species, besides, hybridise in a broad zone in eastern Europe. The most exciting thing I have been able to conjure up is that an occasional individual of the thousands I have studied perhaps had elements of Pine Bunting in its genes.

Grey-green and brownish-red

The Yellowhammer loses its fringes in spring when the darker olive-grey feather tips are abraded and fall off. Many males in this way gradually acquire increasingly more bright yellow areas on the head and some older males finally acquire an almost pure yellow head with only a few dark markings. Most males exhibit a clear border below between smudgy streaks of green umber on the breast sides and an abrupt change into English red on the flanks. The rump is rust-red. I believe that many bird-painters have a weakness for buntings thanks to the latter's intricate feather patterns. There we find many attractive and subdued stripes and colour transitions. Sepia-coloured feather centres, rust-red outer fringes and Naples-yellow edges. It is never tiring to look through a flock of Yellowhammers. The variation and the lovely colours are reward enough.

Can sing up to seven

The Yellowhammer's song is seldom, if ever, heard around the birdtable in the way we often hear the Greenfinch in spring. It is not until the flock breaks up and the males establish territories that we hear the song in its entirety. It is then in the open farmland with juniper and hawthorn, pastureland, woodland edges or clearings with regenerating vegetation where the male sings from the top of a bush. The song is a characteristic simple arithmetic series, one, two, three, four, five, six, seeeven or '*tzi-tzi-tzi-tzi-tzi-tzi-tzuuuuh*'. The first six syllables are fast and slightly buzzing, insect-like, the last drawn out and more clear in tone. Counting out the Yellowhammer's song is a good way of teaching other people about birds, which can trigger an interest in ornithology. In winter it is mainly short sharp calls with a particular squeaky tone, '*tzick*' or '*tziih*', that are heard. The Yellowhammer is a sociable bird which lives in dense flocks and we rarely see any squabbling over food. The younger birds, however, can sometimes chase one another as if in play, and rippling rolling '*prillillillill*' and piercing '*tzick*' calls are then heard. I do not think that I have ever seen Greenfinches or thrushes play, but Yellowhammers at times behave in a way that must be interpreted as play, even if the purpose of the play is to maximise efficiency when faced with attacking Sparrowhawks.

CORN BUNTING

Emberiza calandra

THE CORN BUNTING is clearly bigger than the Yellowhammer. A grey-buff young female Yellowhammer can be similar, but the Corn Bunting has a considerably larger and more powerful bill and the colour is more uniformly greyish-buff. For somebody used to seeing Yellowhammers the Corn Bunting appears as an overgrown bird with a disproportionately large bill. The bill is horn-coloured, whereas the Yellowhammer has a grey-blue tinge on the upper mandible.

In Sweden this species breeds only in south Scania. Occasional singing birds are seen in other parts in spring, but in winter it is a south Scanian bird, with its main occurrence east of Ystad. In north Europe it is tied to the open agricultural landscape and is common in Denmark and down through the Continent in suitable habitats. It is a resident and is readily drawn to grain and seeds which are put out and therefore is one of the species recorded at feeding stations, restricted to a few places. The number of pairs is at most one hundred.

Like many farmland birds, the Corn Bunting was severely hit by insecticides and by the mercury-treated sowings during the 1960s. When I first looked for the species in west Scania at the end of the 1960s, the number of breeding pairs could be counted on the fingers of one hand. After having then almost disappeared from the Swedish fauna, its numbers have slowly increased owing to, among other things, deliberate protective measures together with winter feeding. At the end of the breeding season, Corn Buntings gather in flocks which forage mainly on stubblefields and grasslands and can then collect in considerable numbers.

winter

LITERATURE

Aronsson, Niklas. 2006. *Mata fåglar.*
Bengtsson, Kenneth (ed.) 2009. *Skånsk vinterfågelatlas* 2006–2008.
Blomgren, Arne. 1964. *Lavskrika.*
Borch Grell, Michael. 1998. *Fuglenes Danmark.*
Brusewitz, Gunnar. 1970. *Skissbok.*
Coombs, Franklin. 1978. *The Crows. A study of the Corvids of Europe.*
Haftorn, Svein. 1971. *Norges Fugler.*
Lack, David. 1953. *The Life of the Robin.*
von Linné [Linnaeus], Carl. 1732. *Iter Lapponicum.*
Linnman, Nils. 1954. *Våra fågelvänner.*
Lundgren, Svante. 1949. *Stiglöst land.*
Nilsson, Sven. 1858. *Skandinavisk fauna. Foglarna, tredje utgåvan* [third edition].
Ottosson, Ulf (*et al.*). 2012. *Fåglarna i Sverige. Antal och förekomst.*
Perrins, Christopher M. (ed.) 1994. *Handbook of the birds of Europe, the Middle East, and North Africa. The birds of the western Palearctic.*
von Rosen, Björn. 1968. *Om naturtrohet och andra funderingar om konst.*
Rosenberg, Erik. 1953. *Fåglar i Sverige.*
Svensson, Sören (*et al.*). 1999. *Svensk fågelatlas.*
Svorkmo-Lundberg, Torkild (*et al.*). 2006. *Norsk vinterfuglatlas. Fuglenes utbredelse, bestandsstørrelse og økologi vintertid.*
Valkama, Jari (*et al.*). 2014. *Suomen rengastusatlas. The Finnish bird ringing atlas*, second volume.
von Wright, Magnus. 1859. *Finlands foglar. Hufvudsakligen till deras drägter.*

INDEX